The Illustrated herbal

The Illustrated Herbal

Wilfrid Blunt
Sandra Raphael

THAMES AND HUDSON

*'Furthermore I desire, that none would rashly censure me for that which
I have here done; but they that know in what time I did it.'*
    Thomas Johnson, 'To the Reader', Gerard's *Herball*, second edition, 1633.

Frontispiece
Dioscorides *De Materia Medica* (*Codex Vindobonensis*)
Epinoia (Intelligence) holding up a mandrake
for Krateuas to paint.

Contents

List of Plates

6

7

To Maundy, Poppy,
and Gabriel

Foreword

When two authors combine to produce a book, it has always seemed to me to be desirable to know what part each played. The actual writing of the whole text of *The Illustrated Herbal*, with the exception of the final part dealing with the metal-engraved herbals, was carried out by myself during last winter; but if at first sight this might appear to have been the lion's share, I can assure you that it was not.

First, the lion had to be fed regularly. While I have sat, warm and comfortable in my den in snow-bound darkest Surrey, Sandra Raphael, half my age and ten times more mobile, has examined and reported on numerous herbals in English libraries. A few of these I have never seen, while certain others have grown rather dim in my memory since I last saw them, thirty years ago now, when I was writing my *Art of Botanical Illustration* (Collins, 1950). I was then fortunate enough to have had both time and opportunity to inspect libraries in France, Belgium, Holland, Germany, and Italy, and at a later date I also visited some in America.

Sandra Raphael also did most of the background research necessary to supplement my earlier exploration of the subject, and provided photocopies of many relevant periodical articles and other printed sources. Further, she found answers to endless queries, wrote the section on the metal-engraved herbals, listed the details of the illustrations we chose together, and compiled the bibliography and the index. Each of us read and criticized the text written by the other. I think it was a fair division of labour, and our friendship appears to have survived the arrangement.

W.J.W.B.
Compton, February 1979

Foreword to the Revised Edition

Wilfrid Blunt died in January 1987, so I have revised *The Illustrated Herbal* alone. I have added details of discoveries made since the book's first publication fifteen years ago, as well as the results of recent work on some of the manuscripts and printed books described. I have also revised and extended the bibliography.

During the last twenty years fine facsimiles of the manuscripts of outstanding illustrated herbals have been published, while some of the watercolours made to accompany an unfinished seventeenth-century herbal, Gesner's *Historia Plantarum*, have been printed for the first time. The study of early herbals goes on and will surely add still more to our knowledge of these beautiful books and manuscripts.

S.J.R.
Oxford, February 1994

Introduction

What is a herbal?

According to the *Oxford English Dictionary* it is 'a book containing the names and descriptions of herbs, *or of plants in general*, with their properties and virtues' (our italics). 'Herb',[1] however, is there defined as '1. A plant of which the stem does not become woody and persistent ... but dies down to the ground (or entirely) after flowering. 2. Applied to plants of which the leaves, or stem and leaves, are used for food or medicine, or for their scent or flavour.'

Charles Singer[2] defines the herbal more irreverently:

A *Herbal* is a collection of descriptions of plants put together for medical purposes. Most herbal remedies are quite devoid of any rational basis. It may be taken for granted that the writer of a herbal is unable to treat evidence on a scientific basis. He makes a 'direct attack' on disease, without any 'nonsense about theories'. The herbal is thus to be distinguished from the scientific botanical treatise by the fact that its aims are exclusively 'practical' – a vague and foolish word with which, from the days of Plato to our own, men have sought to conceal from themselves and from others their destitution of anything in the nature of general ideas.

For our present purpose it is convenient to define a herbal as a work dealing primarily with *useful*, or allegedly useful, plants, leaving 'florilegium' for one concerned chiefly with plants grown more for their beauty than for their utility.

Inevitably it is impossible to draw any firm line between the two. The medieval garden, which contained a large majority of

1 In America the 'h' is silent, and a hundred years ago the word was also as often as not pronounced 'erb' in England. I remember, in my childhood, old people in this country, including the educated, who still said 'erb' and 'umble', and now 'umour' and 'otel' are fighting a losing battle for survival here. (W.J.W.B.)

2 Singer (1927), p. 1. NB for references given thus, see the bibliography.

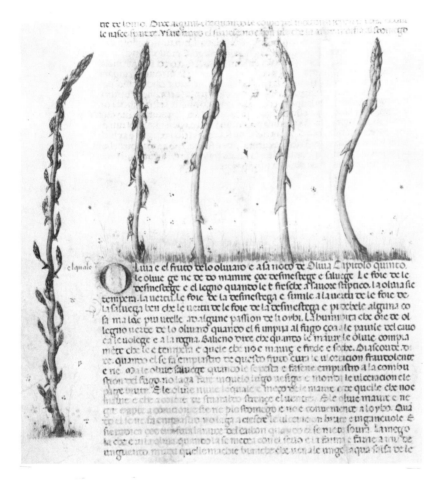

Serapion the Younger *Herbolario volgare, MS. Egerton 2020*, Asparagus (*Asparagus officinalis*), f3v.

useful plants, included some – for example, the rose and the lily – which were given a place as much for their beauty or their religious associations as for their proclaimed 'virtues' or genuine edibility. Similarly, when in the sixteenth century emphasis began to be laid on what we would today call garden plants rather than herbs, the latter continued for many years to be strongly represented in florilegia.

Dr Agnes Arber, in her invaluable book on herbals,[1] deals principally with the *printed* herbal and sets 1470–1670 as her limits. This accounts for her dismissal of the early manuscript herbals in a brief introduction, and for the exclusion of a number of eighteenth-century works actually entitled herbals although the word is used more loosely in some of them. We have, for example, W. Salmon's *Botanologia: the English Herbal* (1710); J. P. de Tournefort's *The Compleat Herbal* (1718–30) – a translation of his *Élémens de Botanique* of 1694; Elizabeth Blackwell's *A Curious Herbal* (1736–39), and P. Bulliard's *Herbier de la France* (1780–93). We must, however, draw a line somewhere, and we do not propose to include the vast quantities of practical books on herbs, many of them of a popular kind though often pleasantly illustrated, published as a result of the relatively recent revival of interest in them.

Finally, as the title of our book suggests, our principal concern is with the pictures which illustrate the herbals rather than with their texts or the virtues of the plants represented. Moreover, many herbals also contain bestiaries and other non-botanical material,[2] to which no more than a passing reference can be made. Particular attention has been given to manuscripts, as being far less familiar to the general reader than are the printed herbals.

1 Arber (1938, reprinted with an introduction and annotations by W. T. Stearn, 1986).

2 It is interesting to note that in every civilization the delineation of plants followed tardily upon the much more difficult art of portraying animals.

The Manuscript Herbals

The First Herbalists

Curiosity about plants must have originated in a concern as to their potential value as food or medicine, and to curiosity was soon to be added superstition.

Primitive man approached the problem empirically, and indeed even today, with all the vast knowledge now available to us, the prescription of drugs by doctors often involves a certain amount of trial and error before that best suited to the needs of a particular patient is established. No one will ever know how many of our forefathers were killed by the alluring fly agaric fungus before its deadly effects became common knowledge, thenceforth to be passed on by herbalists from generation to generation.

To stray for a moment into the field of zoology, there is in the Watts Gallery at Compton a gloriously absurd painting by George Frederick Watts, entitled 'The First Oyster, BC'. It shows a naked youth and maiden seated by the sea-shore. The youth has sampled an oyster, and to judge from his puzzled expression and the way he places his hand on his stomach he is far from certain whether or not he has acted wisely. The blue-eyed Nordic maiden gazes apprehensively and rather fatuously at him as she awaits his verdict.[1] Watts might just as well have painted 'The First Asparagus, BC' with a bronzed Grecian youth discovering whether or not it alleviated the discomfort of what Dioscorides was to call 'the Dysureticall, Ictericall, Nephriticall, and Ischiadicall as also such as are bitten of ye Phalanx [spider]'.[2]

By the time we reach Aristotle, Plato's pupil, who lived in the fourth century BC, botany had become an integral part of natural philosophy as well as a utilitarian pursuit. Aristotle held that plants had a 'psyche' or 'soul', but one of an order lower than that of man and other animals. The precise status and limitations of the psyche of a plant continued to tease botanists and philosophers until the Renaissance. In the thirteenth century Bartholomaeus Anglicus wrote in his *De Proprietatibus Rerum*: 'For trees meve [move] not wylfully fro place to place as beestes doo: nother chaunge appettite and lykynge, nother felyth sorowe ... In tres is soule of lyfe ... but therein is no soule of felynge;'[3] and Albertus Magnus (1193 or 1206–80) was still perplexed as to whether, for example, the souls of the ivy and of the tree to which it clung were united.

Aristotle's pupil, successor and the inheritor of his library was Theophrastus (b. 370 BC), whose botanical work is far better known to us than that of his master since a manuscript entitled *Enquiry into Plants*, probably compiled from his lecture notes, has survived and is available in a translation made by Sir Arthur Hort and published in 1916. Though Theophrastus was principally concerned with the flora of the eastern Mediterranean, he also discussed 'the plants of rivers, marshes and lakes, especially in Egypt' as well as those 'special to northern regions'. Where Egypt is concerned he was no doubt assisted by trained observers known to have accompanied Alexander the Great, also a pupil of Aristotle, on his expeditions.[4]

In the Ninth Book of the *Enquiry*, probably added after his

1 Watts painted the picture after learning that it was being said of him that he had no sense of humour. One is still left in doubt, and he was far from amused when asked whether 'BC' stood for 'Before Clothing'.
2 *The Greek Herbal of Dioscorides* in the charming translation made in 1655 by John Goodyear, edited by Robert T. Gunther, (1934).

3 Trevisa's translation, printed by Wynkyn de Worde c. 1495. Sir Jagadis Bose, in his *Plant Autographs and their Revelations* (1927), demonstrated on his 'Death Recorder' the convulsions of a cabbage as it was being scalded to death – something that horrified Bernard Shaw but which is conveniently overlooked by most vegetarians.
4 Nearchus, one of Alexander's principal admirals, left an excellent description of the banyan tree or Indian fig (*Ficus benghalensis*), various species of mangrove on the islands of the Persian Gulf, and the great spiny euphorbias of Baluchistan. See Singer (1923), p. 98.

death, Theophrastus is described as pulling the leg of the rhizotomists,[1] or herb-gatherers – for the most part ignorant men who recommended such absurdities as digging up the root of the peony only by night, because were they to do it by day a woodpecker would pick out their eyes. But the height of superstition was reached with the mandrake,[2] whose root, sometimes naturally forked but more often faked, was much valued for its alleged likeness to a male or female human being; the resemblance is in fact slight, and few men can ever have been tempted to accept Donne's challenge to 'get with child a mandrake root'. For instance, 'One should draw three circles round mandrake with a sword, and cut it with one's face towards the west; and at the cutting of the second piece one should dance round the plant.'

Over the centuries a whole encyclopaedia of grotesque legends was to grow up around mandrakes, which shrieked when 'torn out of the earth, that living mortals, hearing them, run mad' (*Romeo and Juliet*). Gerard, himself often credulous but quick to ridicule the credulity of others, wrote, 'They fable further and affirm that he who woulde take vp a plant thereof must tie a dogge thereunto to pull it vp, which will giue a great shrike at the digging vp; otherwise if a man should do it, he should certainly die in a short space after.'[3] The dog it was that died, and an illustration in the *Codex Vindobonensis* shows Dioscorides receiving a root of a mandrake from Euresis, the Goddess of Discovery, with the dog in the last stages of convulsions.

But to return to Theophrastus, what concerns us here is whether any of the manuscripts of the *Enquiry* were illustrated. It seems very possible, for we have the evidence of Pliny the Elder[4] that certain herbals at least as early as the beginning of the first century BC were often provided with coloured illustrations, and the practice may well have started before this. Pliny wrote in his *Natural History*:

> *Cratevas* [Krateuas] likewise, *Dionysius* also, and *Metrodorus* . . . painted every hearbe in their colours, and under the pourtraicts they couched and subscribed their severall natures and effects. But what certeintie could there be therein? pictures (you know) are deceitfull; also, in representing such a number of colours, and especially expressing the lively hew of hearbs according to their nature as they grow, no marveile if they that limned and drew them out, did faile and degenerat from the first pattern and originall. Besides, they came far short of the marke, setting out hearbes as they did at one onely season (to wit, either in their floure, or in seed time) for they chaunge and alter their forme and shape everie quarter of the yeare.[5]

Krateuas was physician in ordinary to Mithridates VI, Eupator (King) of Pontus from 120 to 63 BC and himself a herbalist.[6] In writing of the works of Krateuas Pliny was referring to manuscripts with which he was presumably personally familiar; but none survives today. There is little doubt, however, that the designs of Krateuas, the father of botanical illustration, though slowly but steadily degenerating through constant copying, have been in part preserved to us in countless manuscript and printed herbals from the sixth century onwards, while fragments of his

1 Literally 'root-cutters'.

2 For the mandrake see C. J. S. Thompson, *The Mystic Mandrake* (London, 1934) – a fascinating book which tells, among much else, how to manipulate roots to make them look more human, how to keep them in good condition (by a weekly bath on Fridays), and of their innumerable uses: for example, a mandrake tucked in the right armpit of a claimant in a law-suit guarantees its successful issue. More up-to-date information may be found in Stearn (1976).

3 *Herball* (1597), p. 281.

4 Caius Plinius Secundus, generally known as Pliny the Elder, was born in the year AD 23 and perished in 79 when, at the time of the eruption of Vesuvius, which destroyed Pompeii and Herculaneum, his insatiable curiosity and his desire to rescue friends led him to launch his galleys and cross the Bay of Naples to Stabiae (Castellamare).

5 Quoted from Philemon Holland's translation, 1601.
6 According to Pliny, 'The plant *skordion* was described by the Prince's own hand.' Among the other gifts with which this extraordinary man was endowed was a peculiar devotion to medical inquiries. He was an expert on poisons, and the prescription for his panacea to counter their effect has been preserved. 'It may be hoped,' says Dr Singer, 'that his poisons were no more efficacious than his antidote.' Singer (1927), p. 5.

1 Arber (1938), p. 12.

DIOSCORIDES De Materia Medica

(*Codex Vindobonensis*)

Constantinople, *c.* 512

Written in Greek

36–37 × 30 cm ($14\frac{1}{4}$ – $14\frac{1}{2}$ × $11\frac{3}{4}$ in)

491 folios

Österreichische Nationalbibliothek,
Vienna, Med.Gr.1

Colour plates p.18 Opium poppy
(*Papaver somniferum*), f222r; p.19
Bramble (*Rubus fruticosus*), f83r.

2 For an account of other Greek
herbalists of the first century AD see
Singer (1927), pp. 18, 19.
3 Such as the Johnson Papyrus (see
p. 29), and a few yet earlier scraps
(*c.* AD 200?) of a papyrus scroll, also
found in Egypt but too fragmentary
to concern us here. Johnson (1912).
4 There is a good copy (*c.* 1600) of
the illustrations in the University
Library at Cambridge (E.e.5.7). It is
labelled 'Botanicum Antiquum' and
was brought back from Smyrna in
1682.

5 Hence it is also referred to by
some authors as the Juliana Anicia
Codex.
6 Polyeuktes, who was later to
become the hero of a tragedy by
Corneille, lived in the third century.
He was much troubled on the
scaffold that by dying unbaptized he
would not qualify for salvation; but
his friend Nearchus reassured him.

writings were incorporated in the books of later authors, in particular those of Dioscorides.

Pliny's *Natural History* is a vast thesaurus of the accumulated knowledge of his day, in which botany was accorded a substantial space. It is really a compilation, for, as Arber wrote, 'It would scarcely be reasonable to expect much original observation of nature from a man who was so devoted to books, that it was recorded of him that he considered even a walk to be a waste of time.'[1] But he deserves, as she adds, his little niche in the history of botanical terminology since when describing the lily he was the first to use the word 'stamen' in its modern sense.

Undoubtedly the most influential author in the field of herbals in classical times was Pliny's contemporary, Pedianos Dioskurides, generally known to us today as Dioscorides.[2] Born in Asia Minor, he was a medical man, very probably an army doctor, whose *magnum opus*, though written in Greek, is more familiar under its Latin title, *De Materia Medica*. The earliest manuscripts of it appear to have been unillustrated; but there has survived, by an almost unbelievable stroke of good fortune, a magnificent illustrated copy made early in the sixth century, presumably in Constantinople. If we except a few fragments,[3] the *Codex Vindobonensis* of Dioscorides, as it is usually called, is the earliest, and remains by far the most splendid and important, extant illustrated manuscript herbal of classical times,[4] thus obviously constituting the starting-point of our investigations. It seems almost incredible that the influence of Dioscorides, who wrote his *De Materia Medica* in the reigns of Nero and Vespasian, should have persisted until at least the beginning of the nineteenth century.

Over the years his great work was translated into a variety of languages ranging from Anglo-Saxon and Provençal to Persian and Hebrew. Even in the middle of the seventeenth century John Goodyer thought it worthwhile to make an English translation of the whole work, while John Sibthorp, on his way to the Levant to gather material for his *Flora Graeca*, broke his journey in Vienna in 1784 in order to devote many months to a detailed study of the famous *Codex Vindobonensis*. Had Sibthorp been working today he would have been able to make use of the sumptuous facsimile edition published in 1965–70 in five volumes by the Akademische Druck- und Verlagsanstalt in Graz.

So stunning is this great codex, so valuable for the interpretation of plant names used by Dioscorides, so infinitely more impressive than anything that was to be produced for the next one thousand years, that it deserves full description and discussion. It appears that it was written, and illustrated with nearly four hundred full-page coloured paintings of plants, in Constantinople about the year AD 512. The recipient was Juliana Anicia,[5] daughter of Flavius Anicius Olybrius, Emperor of the West in 472 – a Princess who had earned a great reputation for piety by erecting and decorating a church in Constantinople in honour of the martyr Polyeuktes.[6]

In addition to these botanical paintings and a few of birds and other animals, there are, at the beginning, five of a more general nature. One – of Dioscorides receiving a mandrake – has already been mentioned. A second shows six famous botanists with

Dioscorides *De Materia Medica*
(Cambridge copy of illustrations
from *Codex Vindobonensis*), *E.e.5.7,*
Asphodel (*Asphodelus ramosus*), f16r.

Chiron, most learned of the Centaurs. In a third, six famous
doctors, among them Dioscorides and Krateuas, are examining a
patient; at the foot of the page is a serpent. A fourth portrays
Juliana Anicia herself, seated on a throne between allegorical
figures of Wisdom and Magnanimity, while a winged Cupid,
above whom is written 'The Love of the Creator is Wisdom',
presents her with her book and a kneeling figure entitled
Gratitude kisses her feet. In the fifth – perhaps the most
interesting of all – we see Epinoia (Intelligence) holding up a
mandrake for Krateuas to paint.[1] On the left the artist is seated on
a campstool before an easel, both of a kind that might be found in
any studio today; on the right we see Dioscorides at work on his
magnum opus. All five pictures are, unfortunately, damaged.

Nearly nine centuries were to pass before we have further
knowledge of the whereabouts of the codex. Then we learn that
in 1406 it was being rebound by a certain John Chortasmenos for
Nathanael, a monk and physician in the Prodromos Monastery in
Constantinople, where seventeen years later it was seen by a
Sicilian traveller named Aurispa. After the Muslim conquest of
the city in 1453 the codex fell into the hands of the Turks, and
Turkish and Arabic names were then added to the Greek. A
century later it was in the possession of a Jew named Hamon,
body physician to Suleiman the Magnificent, and it was
presumably either by Hamon or by his son, who inherited it, that
Hebrew names were also added.

1 See frontispiece.

15

In 1562, Ogier Ghiselin de Busbecq (1522–92), ambassador from the Emperor Ferdinand to the Sublime Porte, stumbled upon this treasure, and he describes in his letters his unsuccessful attempt to include it in the 'whole waggonfuls, whole shiploads' of Greek manuscripts which he purchased and sent back to Vienna:

> One manuscript I left behind at Constantinople, one much worn with age, containing the whole text of Dioscorides written in capital letters [uncials], with painted representations of plants, among which are a few by Cratevas, unless I am mistaken, as well as a small treatise on birds. This is in the hands of a Jew, the son of Hamon, who while he lived was the doctor of Suleiman. I wished to buy it but the price discouraged me; for it was valued at a hundred ducats, a sum for the Emperor's purse, not for mine. I shall not cease while I have influence with the Emperor to urge him to ransom this noble author from such humiliation. On account of its age the manuscript is in a bad state, the outside being so gnawed by worms, that hardly anyone finding it in the streets would trouble to pick it up.[1]

Busbecq did, however, bring back some drawings of plants for Pierandrea Mattioli,[2] the famous Italian botanist who was physician to the Emperor Ferdinand and his successor Maximilian II, and seven years later the codex found its way into the Imperial Library in Vienna, the purchaser presumably being Maximilian. After the First World War the codex was seized by the Italians and removed to Venice; it was soon returned to the Österreichische Nationalbibliothek, Vienna.

Dioscorides dedicated his book to 'Dearest Areius', his old friend and benefactor, and described the circumstances in which he came to compile it. What he wrote is of such interest where herbals in general are concerned that it deserves quotation at some length:

> Although many writers of modern times, as well as of antiquity, have composed Treatises on the preparation, power and testing of medicines, I will try to show you that I was not moved to this undertaking by any vain or senseless impulse. It was because some of these authors did not perfect their work, while others derived most of their account from histories . . .

After naming some of these offenders, and also criticizing their foolish system of classifying their plants, he continues:

> But we, as I may say from our first growth, having an unceasing desire to acquire knowledge of this matter, and having travelled much (for you know that I led a soldier's life), have by your advice gathered together all that I have commented hereupon, and I have committed it into five books. This compilation I dedicate to you, thus fulfilling my grateful affection for the goodwill you have towards us . . .
>
> But I beg that you, and all who may peruse these Commentaries, will not pay attention so much to the force of our words, as to the industry and experience that I have brought to bear on the matter. For with very accurate

1 Translated by William T. Stearn, *British Delphinium Society Year Book*, 1949, pp. 1–15.
2 See p. 132.

diligence, knowing most herbs with mine own eyes, others by Historical relation agreeable to all, and by questioning, diligently enquiring of the Inhabitants of each sort, we will endeavour both to make use of another arrangement, and also to describe the kinds and forces of every one of them.

There follows the recommendation to gather the herbs only when the weather is fine, and to study their growth at all seasons of the year:

Now it behoves anyone who desires to be a skilful herbalist, to be present when the plants first shoot out of the earth, when they are fully grown, and when they begin to fade. For he who is only present at the budding of the herb, cannot know it when full-grown, nor can he who hath examined a full-grown herb, recognise it when it has only just appeared above ground. Owing to changes in the shape of leaves and the size of stalks, and of the flowers and fruit, and of certain other known characteristics, a great mistake has been made by some who have not paid proper attention to them in this manner. For this very reason, some authors have blundered when they have written of some plants that they bear neither flowers, nor stalk, nor fruit, citing Gramen, Tussilago and Quinquefolium. Therefore the man who will observe his herbs oftentimes and in divers places, will acquire the greatest knowledge of them.

Finally he discusses which herbs can be stored for many years after gathering, and which soon lose their efficacy; how and when to collect roots, bark, petals and juices, and the manner of preserving them:

Flowers and sweet-scented things should be laid up in dry boxes of Lime-wood; but there are some herbs which do well enough if wrapped up in papers or leaves for the preservation of their seeds. For moist medicines some thicker material such as silver, or glass, or horn will agree best. Yes, and earthenware if it be not thin is fitting enough, and so is wood, particularly if it be box-wood. Vessels of brass will be suitable for eye-medicines and for liquids and for all that are compounded of vinegar or of liquid pitch or of Cedria, but fats and marrows ought to be put up in vessels of tin.[1]

Splendid though the figures in the *Codex Vindobonensis* are, they reveal a naturalism so alien to contemporary Byzantine art that it is obvious that they were *not* drawn from nature but derived from originals of a much earlier date – as early, at least, as the second century AD. They vary, however, very much in quality and are clearly not all by the same hand, possibly not even all after the work of a single artist. In the text accompanying eleven of them[2] there is association with the writings[3] of Krateuas. All these figures are admirable, and clearly by the same hand; it must therefore seem certain that they, at all events, are derived from drawings by Krateuas himself.

In a very useful appendix to Goodyer's translation, Gunther has listed all the illustrations, marking them variously from

1 Gunther (1934), pp. 1–4.

2 The 'Greater' and 'Round Aristolochia' (*Aristolochia semper-virens* and *A. pallida*) 'Achilleios' (*Salvia multifida*) 'Purple Anemone' (*Papaver dubium*) 'Asphodel' (*Asphodelus* sp.) 'Argemone' (*Adonis aestivalis*) 'Arnoglosson' (*Plantago* sp.) 'Asaron' (*Asarum europaeum*) 'Asterion' (*Silene linifolia*) and the 'Two Anagallides' (*Anagallis arvensis* and *A. foemina*).

3 His *Rhizotomikon*, known to us only from fragments incorporated in the works of others. It would, of course, have been in the form of a scroll, not of a codex.

Ο ΙΛΟ
ΡΩΜΑΙΟΙ

ΜΗΚΩΝ Η ΜΘΑΛΟ
ΤΕΝΥΓΑ ΘΟΡΙΝ

خشخاش برّی

19

'good', 'pretty good' (for example, that of the opium poppy), 'some resemblance' and so on, down to 'no resemblance' and, finally, 'fictitious'. (But why, one wonders, should the unfortunate 'Malache agria', *Malva sylvestris*, alone be condemned as 'very rude'!) The feeblest figures reveal the evils resulting from incompetent copying and re-copying – a process which was to persist with increasingly disastrous results throughout the Dark and Middle Ages. This sad decline was not to be more than momentarily arrested until the very end of the fourteenth century, and no corpus of illustrations of plants of comparable merit to the *Codex Vindobonensis* is found until Andrea Amadio made his exquisite drawings for Benedetto Rinio in 1419.[1]

1 See p. 73 and colour plates pp. 74–75.

Perhaps the most impressive (and hence the most frequently reproduced) of all the paintings in the *Codex Vindobonensis* is that of 'Batos' (bramble – *Rubus fruticosus*). After mentioning other names by which the plant is sometimes known, Dioscorides lists its virtues; and, as always, almost every plant is alleged to be an infallible cure for almost every ill. Batos, he says,

> binds and drys; it dyes ye hair. But the decoction of the tops of it being drank stops ye belly, & restrains ye flux of women, & is convenient for ye biting of ye Prester. And the leaves being chewed do strengthen ye gums, and heal ye Apthae. And ye leaves being applied, do restrain ye Herpetas, & heal ye running ulcers which are in ye head, & ye falling down of the eyes . . .

They were no less efficacious for the condylomata and haemorrhoids, and for stomach and cardiac troubles when 'beaten small, & and so laid on', but the juice obtained by bruising the stalks and leaves and stirring it in the sun was even more effective. The juice of the ripe fruit made a good 'mouth medicine', while that of the half-ripe fruit, or the flowers infused in wine, 'doth also stop ye belly'. There is no mention of other than medicinal properties – for example, that ripe blackberries are nice to eat.

Dioscorides criticized the system of classification adopted by his predecessors, but his own – such as it was – was not appreciably better. Sometimes plants are grouped according to their habit of growth, with the result (as Singer observes) that various members of certain groups now recognized as families – for example, the Labiatae, Papilionaceae, Umbelliferae, and Compositae – tend to fall together. However, it also results in his placing chamomile (a composite) among the umbellifers. He mentions some five hundred plants, about 130 of which had already been discussed in the so-called *Hippocratic Collection*, a corpus of very early Greek fragments of botanical writings; thus more than a quarter of these drugs had by then been in use for several centuries.

Singer lists forty-four drugs mentioned by Dioscorides that have survived in the 'modern official pharmacopoeias of civilised Europe', passing to us through the Middle Ages either continuously or in early Renaissance translations. Of all these, he comments, 'only about a quarter have any definite pharmacological action. The remainder are diluents, flavouring agents, emollients and the like.'[2]

2 Singer (1927), p. 22.

20

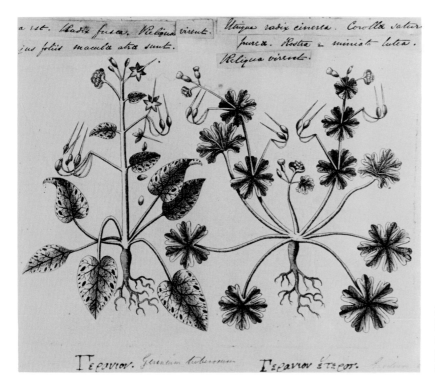

Dioscorides *De Materia Medica* (Oxford copy of illustrations from *Codex Neapolitanus*) Geraniums (*Erodium malacoides* and *Geranium molle*).

Of the many other surviving illustrated Greek manuscripts of Dioscorides,[1] next in importance is probably the seventh-century *Codex Neapolitanus*. It seems that this codex, which had long been in the possession of the monks of a Neapolitan monastery, was presented by them in 1717 to the Emperor Charles VI and taken to Vienna; but after the First World War the Italians recovered it and it is now in the Biblioteca Nazionale in Naples.

Its drawings, which are derived from the same source as those in the *Codex Vindobonensis* and owe nothing to the direct observation of nature, do not at first sight appear to be so very inferior to the figures in the earlier and more famous work; but a closer inspection shows them to be one degree further removed from the long lost prototypes. Unlike those in the Vienna codex they are small, and grouped several together on a single page; but through this arrangement they acquire a certain decorative quality. Latin names of the plants have been added.

A series of more than four hundred uncoloured engravings after paintings in the *Codex Vindobonensis* and the *Codex Neapolitanus*[2] was made by order of the Empress Maria Teresa (1717–80).[3] It is said that only four copies were printed: two were presented by Baron Nikolaus von Jacquin, the director of the Botanic Garden, to Linnaeus and Sibthorp. Linnaeus's copy, after being in the possession of Sir James Edward Smith, is now in the Library of the Linnean Society, London; Sibthorp's, which contains many more plates than the Linnean one, had the Greek names of the plants added by its owner, who presented it to the Botany School of Oxford. The vast majority of the engravings, which are rather mechanical in quality, are taken from the *Codex Neapolitanus*.

A brave attempt at a monochrome facsimile of the *Codex Vindobonensis* was produced in two bulky volumes by J. von Karabacek in Leiden in 1906; this has, of course, now been superseded by the splendid Graz publication already mentioned.

DIOSCORIDES De Materia Medica

(*Codex Neapolitanus*)

Seventh century

Written in Greek

29.4 × 24.9 cm ($11\frac{1}{2}$ × $9\frac{3}{4}$ in)

172 folios

Biblioteca Nazionale, Naples, MS.Gr.1

Colour plates p.22 Lady's bedstraw (*Galium verum*), cranesbill (*Erodium malacoides*) and *Geranium molle*, f58r; p.23 Winter cherry (*Physalis alkekengi*) and mulleins (*Verbascum* sp.), f148.

1 For the relationship of the various manuscripts of Dioscorides see chart on p.52.

2 Then in Vienna.

3 Jackson (1916–17).

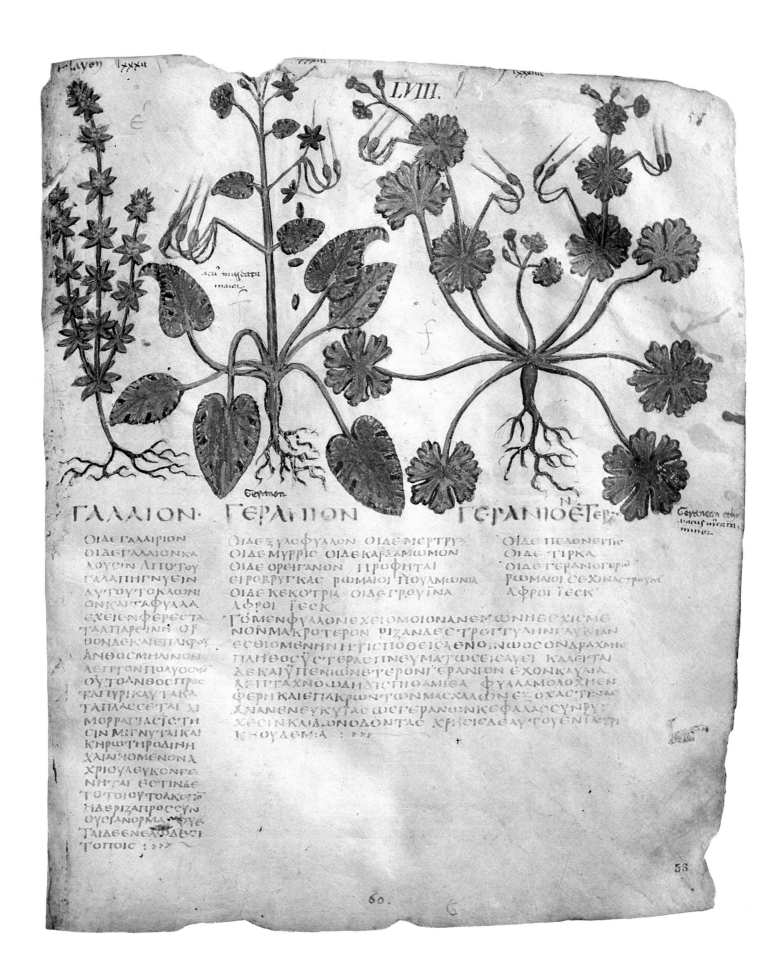

ΓΑΛΛΙΟΝ·   ΓΕΡΑΝΙΟΝ   ΓΕΡΑΝΙΟΕΤΕ

ΟΙΔΕ ΓΑΛΛΙΡΙΟΝ   ΟΙΔΕ ΞΥΛΟΦΥΛΛΟΝ ΟΙΔΕ ΜΕΡΤΡΥΞ   ΟΙΔΕ ΠΕΛΟΝΕΙΤΙΣ
ΟΙΔΕ ΓΑΛΛΙΟΝ ΚΑ   ΟΙΔΕ ΜΥΡΡΙΣ ΟΙΔΕ ΚΑΡΔΑΜΩΜΟΝ   ΟΙΔΕ ΤΙΡΚΑ
ΛΟΥΣΙΝ ΑΠΟΤΟΥ   ΟΙΔΕ ΟΡΕΙΓΑΝΟΝ ΠΡΟΦΗΤΑΙ   ΟΙΔΕ ΓΕΡΑΝΙΟΓΕΡ
ΓΑΛΑΠΗΓΝΥΕΙΝ   ΕΙΡΟΚΡΥΓΚΑΣ ΡΩΜΑΙΟΙ ΠΟΥΑΜΩΝΙΑ   ΡΩΜΑΙΟΙ ΣΕΧΙΝΑΣΤΡΟΥΜ
ΑΥΤΟΥ ΤΟ ΚΛΩΝΙ   ΟΙΔΕ ΚΕΚΟΤΡΙΑ ΟΙΔΕ ΓΡΟΥΙΝΑ   ΑΦΡΟΙ ΙΕΣΚ
ΟΝ ΚΑΙ ΤΑ ΦΥΛΛΑ   ΑΦΡΟΙ ΙΕΣΚ
ΕΧΕΙ ΕΜΦΕΡΕΣΤΑ   ΓΟ ΜΕΝ ΦΥΛΛΟΝ ΕΧΕΙ ΟΜΟΙΟΝ ΑΝΕΜΩΝΗ ΕΣΧΙΣΜΕ
ΤΑ ΑΠΑΡΕΙΝΗ ΟΙ   ΝΟΝ ΜΑΚΡΟΤΕΡΟΝ ΡΙΖΑΝ ΔΕ ΣΤΡΟΓΓΥΛΗΝ ΓΛΥΚΙΑΝ
ΘΟΝ ΔΕ ΚΑΙ ΕΠΑΚΡΟΥ   ΕΣΘΙΟΜΕΝΗΝ ΗΤΙΣ ΠΟΘΕΙΣ ΛΕΝΟ, ΝΩ ΟΣΟΝ ΔΡΑΧΜΗΣ
ΑΝΘΟΣ ΜΗΛΙΝΟΝ   ΠΛΗΘΟΣ ΥΣΤΕΡΑΣ ΠΝΕΥΜΑΤΩΣΕΙΣ ΑΓΕΙ ΚΑΛΕΙΤΑΙ
ΛΕΠΤΟΝ ΠΟΛΥ ΟΣΜΟ   ΔΕ ΚΑΙ ΥΠΕΝΙΩΝ ΕΤΕΡΟΝ ΓΕΡΑΝΙΟΝ ΕΧΟΝ ΚΑΥΛΙΑ
ΟΥ ΤΟ ΑΝΘΟΣ ΠΡΟΣ   ΛΕΠΤΑ ΧΝΟΩΔΗ ΔΑΣΥΠΟΘΑΜΙΕΑ ΦΥΛΛΑ ΜΟΛΟΧΗΣ
ΓΡΑΠΥΡΙ ΚΑΥΤΑ ΚΑ   ΦΕΡΗ ΚΑΙ ΕΠ ΑΚΡΩΝ ΤΩΝ ΜΑΣΧΑΛΩΝ ΕΣΟΧΑΣ ΤΕΝΑ
ΤΑ ΠΑΣΣΕΤΑΙ ΑΙ   ΧΛΑ ΑΝΕΝΕΥΚΥΤΑΣ ΩΣ ΓΕΡΑΝΩΝ ΚΕΦΑΛΑΣ ΣΥΝ ΡΥΓ
ΜΟΡΡΑΓΙΑΣ ΙΣΤΗ   ΧΕΣΙΝ ΚΛΙΔΛΟΝΟΔΟΝΤΑΣ ΧΡΗΣΙΣ ΔΕ ΑΥΤΟΥ ΕΝ ΙΑΤΡΙ
ΣΙΝ ΜΙΓΝΥΤΑΙ ΚΑΙ   ΚΗ ΟΥΔΕΜΙΑ : ⁊⁊⁊
ΚΗΡΩΤΗΡ ΟΔΙΝΗ
ΧΛΑΙΝΟΜΕΝΟΝ Α
ΧΡΙ ΟΥ ΛΕΥΚΟΝ ΓΕ
ΝΗΤΑΙ ΕΣΤΙ ΔΕ
ΤΟΤΟΙΟΥΤΟ ΛΚΟΤΙΟ
ΗΔΕ ΡΙΖΑ ΠΡΟΣ ΣΥΝ
ΟΥΣΙΑΝ ΟΡΜΑΣΥΕ
ΤΑΙ ΔΕ ΕΝ ΕΛΩΔΕΣΙ
ΤΟΠΟΙΣ : ⁊⁊⁊

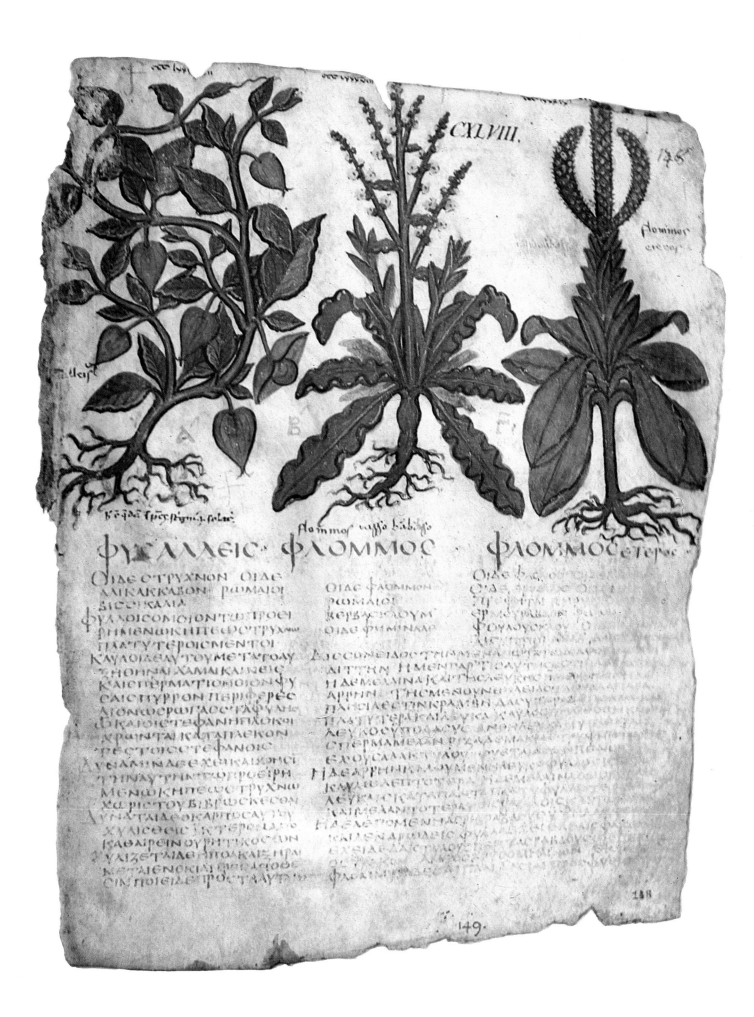

ΦΥΣΑΛΛΕΙΣ· ΦΛΟΜΜΟΣ   ΦΛΟΜΜΟCετεροс

Dioscorides *De Materia Medica, MS. Grec 2179*, Castor-oil plant (*Ricinus communis*), f131v.

DIOSCORIDES De Materia Medica
Egypt, ninth century
Written in Greek
Bibliothèque Nationale, Paris,
MS.Grec 2179
Colour plate p.26 Grape hyacinth
(*Muscari* sp.) and poppy (*Papaver* sp.), f90v.

In the Bibliothèque Nationale in Paris is a Dioscorides, written in Greek in Egypt in the ninth century, with figures that for the most part are naturalistic though all derived from earlier manuscripts. It is in a very battered condition, but a copy of it in the Marciana in Venice (273), made in the eleventh century, enables us to supply what is defective.

Some of the illustrations are taken, directly or indirectly, from those in the *Codex Vindobonensis*; others, however, do not relate to those in any other known manuscript. The castor-oil plant, *Ricinus communis*, closely resembles the admirable figure of it in the Vienna codex, though lacking its subtlety. The Paris codex contains three figures of mandrakes possibly unique among medieval renderings of the plant in that they have no anthropomorphic features. This, says Singer, cannot be attributed to wisdom on the part of the ninth-century artist because his 'Lochitis' – a plant impossible to identify – has three flowers with crudely drawn human faces. He suggests, therefore, that some of its figures may be the only surviving record of certain naturalistic prototypes of classical times.[1]

1 Singer (1927), pp. 28–29.

NIKANDER Alexipharmaka
(Remedies)
Ninth century
Written in Greek
Bibliothèque Nationale, Paris,
Sup.Gr.247

Another ninth-century Greek herbal, though not having a text by Dioscorides, may perhaps be mentioned here. It illustrates the *Alexipharmaka* of the Greek poet Nikander, who lived about 200 BC and with the exception of Theophrastus is the earliest recorded herbalist. The manuscript is badly damaged, and its figures are obviously copied from lost classical originals.

In 1920, the Pierpont Morgan Library in New York acquired from the Phillipps collection a handsome codex of Dioscorides, the dating of which has puzzled experts. Charles Singer[1] attributes it to the middle of the eleventh century, whereas a more recent authority, Professor Lake, places it about 150 years earlier, considering that it may in fact be Singer's hypothetical 'Q'. Lake bases his dating on the character of the calligraphy, which is a minuscule script in brown ink. At all events it belongs to the so-called 'Secondary Alphabetic Group', in which the plants – like those in the 'Primary Alphabetic Group' that includes both the *Codex Vindobonensis* and the *Codex Neapolitanus* – are listed alphabetically.

Some of the figures in the Pierpont Morgan manuscript, which was also made in Constantinople, are remarkably close to the corresponding ones in the Vienna codex; but others bear little or no resemblance. Where plants are concerned, the former is far less complete than the latter; but it includes a good deal of miscellaneous material – for example, a bestiary, representations of receptacles for oils, wines, and medicines, and so on – which are not to be found in the *Codex Vindobonensis*.

Another manuscript in Rome (Vatican Gr. 284), written about the year 1100, also belongs to the Secondary Alphabetic Group. Professor W. T. Stearn, now President of the Linnean Society of London, has examined a codex in the Lavra monastery on Mount Athos, which belongs to the same group and is probably of roughly the same date. He informs us that the illustrations are also undistinguished.

As is well known, science throughout the Dark and Middle Ages in Europe owes an enormous debt of gratitude to Islamic scholars, who cherished classical learning. The works of Dioscorides and other Greek authors were carried to Asia Minor by Nestorian Christians banished from Europe for their heretical views, and thence disseminated throughout the Muslim world. An Arabic translation of *De Materia Medica* was made, direct from the Greek, by a Christian in Baghdad about 854. Another was prepared at Cordoba in 948 from a copy sent to the Spanish Khalif, Abd-er Rahman III, by the Byzantine Emperor Romanus II; and an illustrated Syriac version, written around the year 1250, gave rise to yet a further version in Arabic. The illustrations, when present, have no obvious relationship with those of the classical line.

An Arabic translation of Dioscorides, dating from the eleventh century, is in the Bibliothèque Nationale, Paris (MS. Arab 4947). A Persian translation, dating from the thirteenth century, is preserved in the Shrine at Meshed (Iran), and a nineteenth-century copy of it was formerly lent by Mrs Leyel to the Society of Herbalists in London. After her death the latter was sold by auction at Sotheby's in July 1958, and its present whereabouts is not known.

The Bodleian Library also has an Arabic Dioscorides (MS. Arab d. 138; Arch. O. d. 9), dated AD 1239. It opens with a portrait of the author, defaced at some time by a pious Muslim but later given a very crudely drawn head in a turban, and contains some two hundred rather indifferent botanical drawings. The plants here shown are two mandrakes.

DIOSCORIDES De Materia Medica
Constantinople(?), ninth century
Written in Greek
39.4 × 27.9 cm (15½ × 11 in)
385 folios
Pierpont Morgan Library, New York, M652
Colour plate p.27 Caraway (*Carum carvi*) and nut grass (*Cyperus esculentus*), f77v.

1 1927, p. 25.

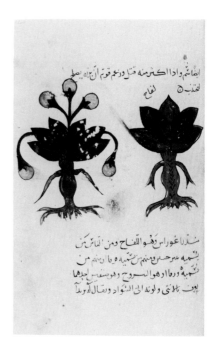

Dioscorides *De Materia Medica*, MS. *Arab d. 138*, Two mandrakes (*Mandragora autumnalis*), f119v.

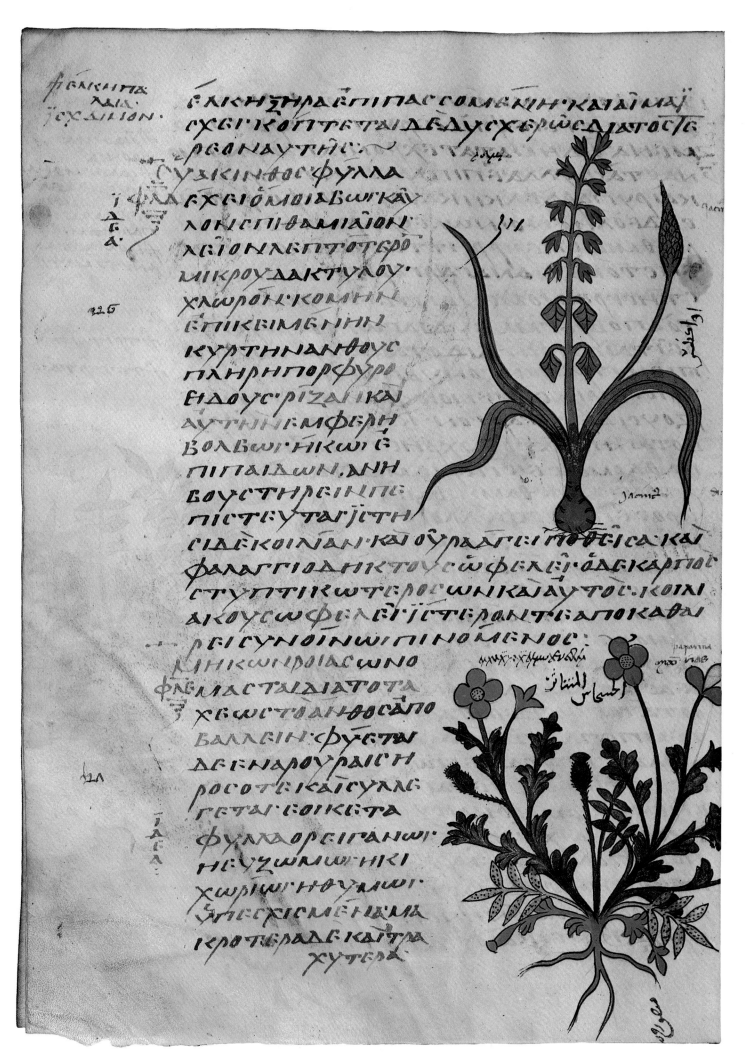

ϵ ΛΚΗ Ϟ ΗΡΑ Ε ΠΙ ΠΑϹ ϹΟΜϵΝΗΝ · ΚΑΙ ΔΙ ΛΑϹ
ϹΧϵ Ι ·ΚΟ ΠΤϵΤΑΙ Δϵ ΔΥ ϹΧϵΡ ῶϹ ΔΙΑ ΤΟ ϹΤϵ
ΡϵΟΝ ΑΥΤΗϹ·

ῙϹΥ ΔΚΙΝΘΟϹ ΦΥΛΛΑ
ϵΧϵΙ Ο ΜΟΙΑ ΒΟΛΚΑΥ
ΛΟΚΙ ΠΙΘΑΜΙΑΙΟΝ
ΛϵΙΟΝ ΛϵΠΤΟΤϵΡΟ
ΜΙΚΡΟΥ ΔΑΚΤΥΛΟΥ·
ΧΛωΡΟΝ · ΚΟΜΗΝ
ϵΠΙΚϵΙΜϵΝΗΝ
ΚΥΡΤΗΝ ΑΝΘΟΥϹ
ΠΛΗΡΗ ΠΟΡΦΥΡΟ
ϵΙΔΟΥϹ · ΡΙΖΑΝ ΚΑΙ
ΑΥΤΗΝ ϵ ΜΦϵΡΗ
ΒΟΛΒω ΠΗ ΚΑΙ Ο ϵ
ΠΙ ΠΑΙΔωΝ · ΔΗΗ
ΒΟΥϹ ΤΗΡϵΙ Η Πϵ
ΠΙϹΤϵΥΤΑΙ ΪϹΤΗ
ϹΙ Δϵ ΚΟΙΛΙΑΝ ΚΑΙ ΟΥΡΑ ΑΓϵΙ Π Ο ϒϹ Ι ϹΑ ΚΑΙ
ΦΑΛΑΓΓΙΟ ΔΗΚΤΟΥϹ ωΦϵΛϵΙ Ο Δϵ ΚΑΡΠΟϹ
ϹΤΥΠΤΙΚωΤϵΡΟϹ ωΝ ΚΑΙ ΑΥΤΟϹ · ΚΟΙΛΙ
ΑΚΟΥϹ ωΦϵΛϵΙ ΪϹΤϵΡΑ Ν Τϵ ΑΠΟΚΑΘΑΙ
ΡϵΙ ϹΥΝ ΟΙΝω ΠΙΝΟΜϵΝΟϹ·

ΛΙΝΚ Κων ΡΟΙΑϹ ωΝΟ
ΦϊΛΛΑϹ ΤΙΛ ΔΙΑ ΤΟ ΤΑ
Χϵ ωϹ Τ ΑΛΗΘΟϹ ΑΠΟ
ΒΑΛΛϵΙΝ · ΦΥϵΤω
Δϵ ϵΝ Α ΡΟΥΡΑΙϹ Η
ΡΟϹΟΤϵΚΑΙ ϹΥΛΛϵ
ΓϵΤΑΙ · ϵΟΙΚϵ ΤΑ
ΦΥΛΛΑ ΟΡϵΙΓΑΝωϊ
Η ΕΥΖωΜωϊ Η ΚΙ
ΧωΡΙωϊ ΗΟ ΥΛΙωϊ·
ϒΠϵϹΧΙϹΜϵΝΗ ΜΑ
ΚΡΟΤϵΡΑ Δϵ ΚΑΙ ΠΛΑ
ΧΥΤϵΡΑ

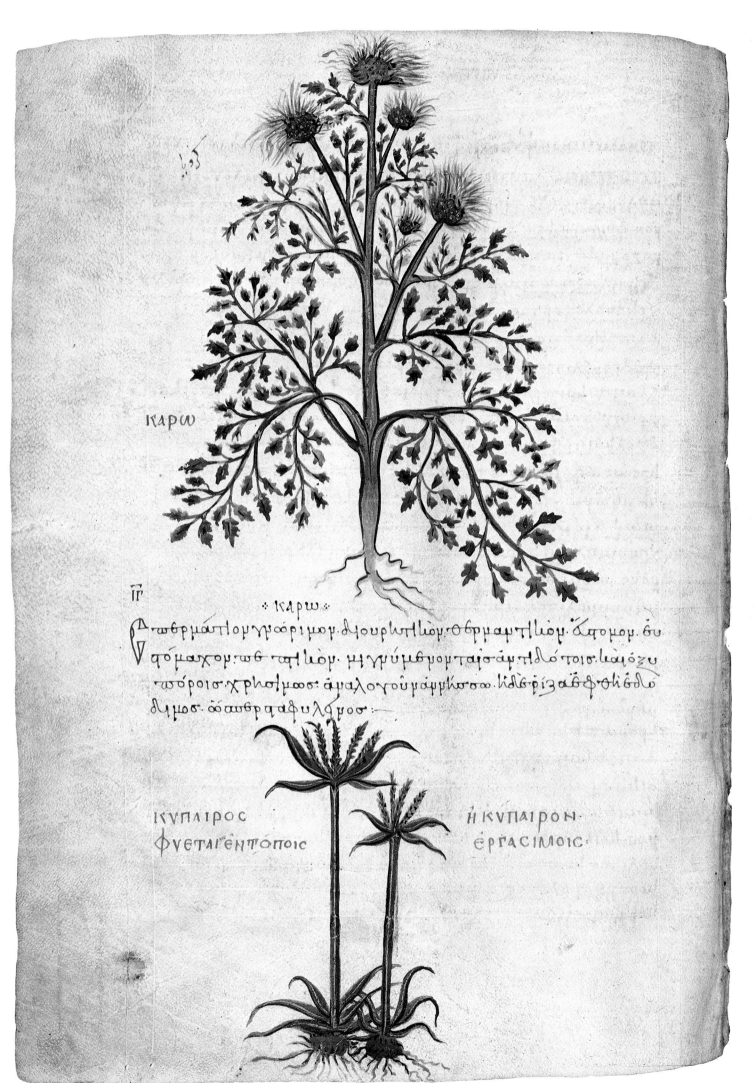

κapω

πΓ

• κapω •

ⲋ ωⲑⲣⲙⲁⲛⲧⲓⲕⲟⲛ γνⲱⲣⲓⲙⲟⲛ· ⲁⲓⲟⲩⲣⲏⲧⲓⲕⲟⲛ· ⲑⲉⲣⲙⲁⲛⲧⲓⲕⲟⲛ· ⲕⲧⲟⲙⲟⲛ· ⲉⲩ
τⲟⲙⲁⲭⲟⲛ· ⲱⲥ ⲁⲣⲧⲓⲟⲛ· ⲏ γⲅⲩⲙⲉⲣⲟⲛ ⲧⲁⲓⲥ ⲁⲣⲧⲏⲗⲟ ⲧⲟⲓⲥ·ⲕⲁⲓ ⲟⲍⲩ
ⲧⲟⲣⲟⲓⲥ· ⲭⲣⲏⲥⲓⲙⲟⲥ· ⲁⲙⲁⲗⲟγⲟⲩⲙⲁⲣⲏⲛⲟⲥ ⲟⲥ ⲕⲓⲃ ⲉ ⲣⲓⲍⲁⲉⲑ ⲑⲓⲉⲃⲗⲟ
ⲗⲩⲙⲟⲥ· ⲟⲟ ⲱⲥ ⲉ ⲣⲧⲁⲫⲩⲗ ⲁⲓⲟⲥ :–

κⲩⲡⲁⲓⲣⲟⲥ   ⲏ ⲕⲩⲡⲁⲓⲣⲟⲛ·
ⲫⲩⲉⲧⲁⲓ ⲉⲛ ⲧⲟⲡⲟⲓⲥ   ⲉ ⲣⲅⲁⲥⲓⲙⲟⲓⲥ·

Apuleius Platonicus *Herbarium*,
Voss. Lat.Q9, Comfrey (*Symphytum*
sp.).

APULEIUS PLATONICUS
Herbarium and other medical texts
Southern Italy or Southern France,
sixth or early seventh century
27×20 cm ($10\frac{5}{8} \times 7\frac{7}{8}$ in)
104 folios
Bibliotheek der Rijksuniversiteit,
Leiden, Voss.Lat.Q9

1 Anderson (1977) p. 29.

Latin manuscripts of Dioscorides, some illustrated, exist; but for
the most part they are combined with the text of a Latin herbal by
a certain Apuleius – usually referred to as Apuleius Barbarus,
Apuleius Platonicus, or Pseudo-Apuleius in order to distinguish
him from the author of *The Golden Ass*. The text, a relatively
worthless compilation of medical recipes, was put together from
Greek material around the year AD 400. Nothing seems to be
known of him beyond his name (see chart on p. 53).

The earliest surviving manuscript of this herbal, now in Leiden,
dates from about 600, but there is good evidence that it was
copied from a codex of two centuries earlier. Its figures are much
inferior to those of the Vienna *Dioscorides*, and, like them, derivative though of different origin; it is, therefore, in spite of being denounced by Singer as 'a futile work, with its unrecognisable
figures and incomprehensible vocabulary', and by Frank J.
Anderson as 'a straw desperately grasped at by despairing men,'[1]
in its way a landmark in the history both of botany and of botanical illustration. It was probably written in the south of France,
and for many generations was unhappily to provide western
illustrators from Italy to the Rhine with a storehouse for plunder.

The different source of the illustrations was probably Greek, evidence for which is provided by the so-called *Johnson Papyrus*. Reference was made earlier (see p. 14) to 'fragments' of botanical illustration pre-dating those in the *Codex Vindobonensis*, among which is the above-mentioned papyrus, now on loan to University College London. This consists of most of a single page of a Greek codex, dating from about AD 400 and originally probably measuring nearly 10 inches in length by a little over 6 inches in breadth,[1] and was discovered by J. de M. Johnson[2] in 1904 while working at Antinoe, in Egypt. Two plants are shown – 'Symphyton' (comfrey) and 'Phlommos' (mullein) – together with some damaged text. These illustrations are clearly associated with those of 'Sinfitos' and 'Verbascum' (a synonym of 'Phlommos') in both the Leiden manuscript and a tenth-century Apuleius now in Kassel (Cod. Phys. fol. 10); that of the 'Verbascum' bears, however, no resemblance whatever to the illustration of the mullein in the *Codex Vindobonensis*, in which comfrey is not provided with a figure.

Johnson Papyrus
c. 400
Written in Greek
Wellcome Institute for the History of Medicine, London

1 Singer (1927) p. 31 gives dimensions in millimetres but obviously means centimetres.
2 Johnson later pursued a very different career as Printer to the University of Oxford. His collection of printed ephemera is now in the Bodleian Library.

Above left and above right
Johnson Papyrus Comfrey (*Symphytum* sp.) and mullein (*Verbascum* sp.).

henne belle

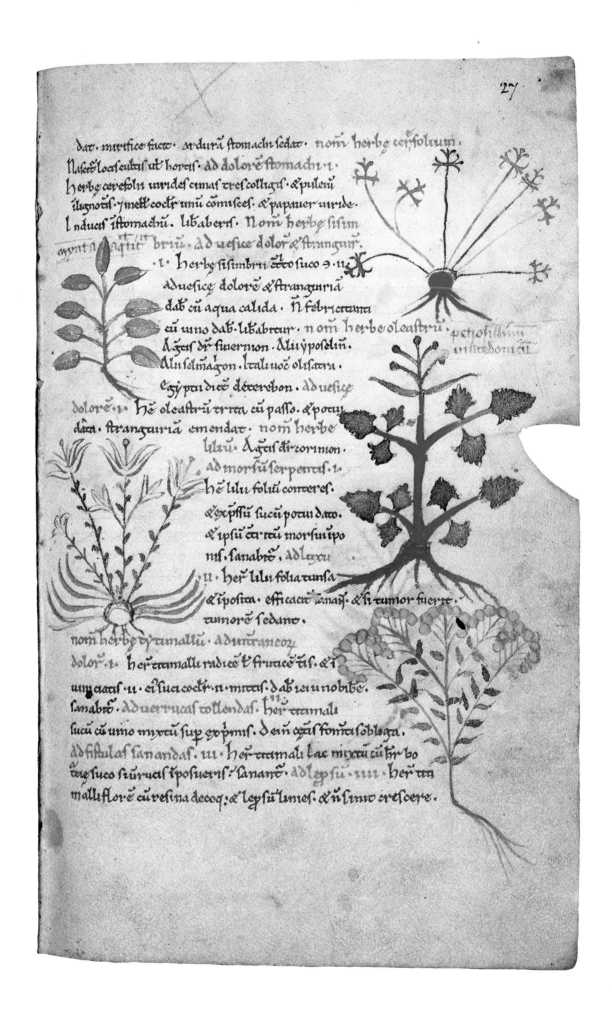

dat. mirtice fuit. ardurā stomachi sedat. nom̄ herbe cerfolium.
Nascit̄ locis cultis ut hortis. ad dolorē stomachi. ı.
herbe cerefolu uirides cimas tres colligis. & pulen
illagnois. ı meti coctr̄ unū comisces. & papauer uiride.
Induceis istomachū. libaberis. Nom̄ herbe sisim
brin. ad uesice dolorē & stranguir.
ı. herbe sisimbrin cōco suco ꝥ ıı.
aduesice dolorē & stranguriā
dab̄ cū aqua calida. n̄ febrieꝛtīt
cū uino dab̄. libabreur. nom̄ herbe oleastrū
Agreis dr̄ sinernion. Alii yposelin.
Alii selmagon. Italii uocē olisatra.
Egypti dicē deterebon. ad uesicē
dolorē. ı. hē oleastrū trita cū passo. & potui
dāta. stranguriā emendat. nom̄ herbe
lilıū. Agreis dr̄ cirorinion.
ad morsū serpentis. ı.
hē lilu foliū conteres.
& expiū sucū potui dato.
& ipsū cōtrū morsuī ipo
nis. sanabis. ad luxu
ıı. her̄ lilu folia tunsa
& iposita. efficacitꝰ sanaꝭ. & si tumor fuerit.
tumorē sedato.
nom̄ herbe tytimallū. ad uulᶠraneoꝝ
dolorē. ı. her̄ tytimalli radicē ꝰ fruticē tis. & ı
uni uicatis. ıı. eı suci coctr̄. ıı. mitteis. dab̄ ieiuno bibe.
sanabis. ad uerrucas tollendas. her̄ tytimali
sucū cū uino mixtū sup ꝓpris. ꝺ eıꝰ cōtꝰ fomentis obliga.
ad fistulas sanandas. ııı. her̄ tytimali lac mixtū cū tι bo
ꝶꝰ suco sūurucis iposueris. sanaꝰ. ad lepsū. ıııı. her̄ ty
malli florē cū resina decoq. & lepsū linies. & u siniu erescere.

The Anglo-Saxon Herbals

Southern Italy, formerly Magna Graecia, was an important centre of botanical learning throughout the Dark and Middle Ages. At Squillace, in Calabria, Cassiodorus (490–583?), Theodoric the Ostrogoth's private secretary, founded on his family estate two monasteries whose monks were encouraged to study and copy classical codices. Among these was said to have been a Latin translation of Dioscorides with figures derived both from Krateuas and from the same source that was to be used again in the Leiden Apuleius.

At a later date and far more influential were the monastery of Monte Cassino, in the Duchy of Beneventum, and the medical school at Salerno near Naples. At Monte Cassino the monks made translations from both Arabic and Greek, and a copy of an important ninth-century manuscript of Apuleius (Codex Casiensis 97) was to influence Anglo-Saxon herbals and provide the model for the first printed edition of Apuleius (Rome 1481?).[1]

It seems probable that the *Herbal of Apuleius* was first translated into Anglo-Saxon about the year 1000. If so, it was the first vernacular translation of a herbal; but no such manuscript has survived. The finely illustrated, though damaged, Anglo-Saxon codex, Cotton Vitellius C. III, which combines elements of both Dioscorides and Apuleius, can be dated around the middle of the eleventh century. Its text appears to have been translated from a manuscript that originated in southern Italy, and some of its figures show features that clearly betray their Mediterranean source. There is, for example, a good representation of a scorpion, and the 'Hennebelle' (henbane)[2] that is illustrated is not a British native. It was little if at all understood in the Middle Ages that species varied from country to country. A comparison of figures in this herbal with illustrations in a tenth-century French manuscript (Bibliothèque Nationale, Paris, MS. Lat. 6862) derived from southern sources, makes the origin of the former plain.

The Cotton Vitellius marks the foundation of a distinctively Anglo-Saxon type of herbal illustration, developed from two different Carolingian styles introduced into England in the previous century. In the one the emphasis is on line, in the other on tone; and the two, as here, are sometimes found side by side in the same manuscript. The henbane has been tenderly painted in blue and green without the use of outline, whereas the wolf's comb or teasel (*Dipsacus fullonum*) shows firm contours. Neither would, of course, have been painted from life.

One Cotton Apuleius has had a stormy passage. A virulent green pigment, probably sulphate of copper, had already damaged the paintings before a disastrous fire at Ashburnham House in 1731 destroyed part of the Cottonian Library and reduced the book to 'a shrivelled lump of leaves'. However, skilful restoration, involving washing, flattening and mounting the vellum pages, has succeeded in rescuing all that was not beyond recovery. The work was carried out by Joseph Planta, keeper of manuscripts at the British Museum from 1776 to 1793.

A blank page (141v) at the end of this very influential codex contains notes in the hand of William Harvey (1578–1657), the distinguished English physician who discovered the circulation of the blood.

1 See p. 113 below, and for the strange fate of one of these figures, that of *Saxifraga granulata*, Blunt (1950) pp. 16, 32 and 35.

APULEIUS PLATONICUS

Herbarium and other medical texts

England, *c.* 1050

Written in Anglo-Saxon

30.5 × 23.5 cm (12 × 9¼ in)

140 folios

British Library, London,

MS. Cotton Vitellius C. III

Colour plate p. 30 Henbane (*Hyoscyamus* sp.), f23v.

2 The so-called 'henbane' is in fact possibly vervain (*Verbena officinalis*), recommended in the text for treating the bite of poisonous spiders, two of which (attercops) and a serpent are shown at the top of the painting. The ghost of an adderwort (*Polygonum bistorta*) has emerged from the back of the page.

Far Left
Apuleius Platonicus *Herbarium,
MS. Cotton Vitellius C. III,* Meadow
saxifrage (*Saxifraga granulata*), f49v.
Left
Herbal of Apuleius Platonicus
(1481 ?), Meadow saxifrage
(*Saxifraga granulata*).

The text and figures of an English mid-twelfth-century herbal confirm the importance of southern Italy during this period. Harley 5294 is also derived from both Dioscorides and Apuleius and shares the same common ancestor as the Cotton Vitellius codex. It is closely connected with a manuscript now in Turin (K IV 3) and written in Beneventan script; the Harleian manuscript, however, has Anglo-Saxon glosses. Our illustration for the herb 'Sanguinaria', showing a man being bitten by a mad dog, also appears in the Turin manuscript.

There is a late eleventh-century English herbal which is illustrated throughout with decorative, stylized plants and which again combines the varied techniques used in the Cotton Vitellius codex. As one or two blank spaces make plain, the figures were added after the text had been written. Both male and female mandrakes are there in anthropomorphic form, the male being as usual attached to a dog by a length of rope. Among the five plants shown in our illustration from this manuscript, Ashmole 1431, is chervil, 'which grows in cultivated places and settles the stomach'.

APULEIUS PLATONICUS
Herbarium
Southern Italy, twelfth century
26 × 17.8 cm (10¼ × 7 in)
68 folios
British Library, London,
MS. Harley 5294

APULEIUS PLATONICUS
Herbarium
Canterbury, England, *c.* 1070–1100
23.5 × 14.5 cm (9¼ × 5¾ in)
44 folios
Bodleian Library, Oxford,
MS. Ashmole 1431
Colour plate p.31 Chervil
(*Chaerophyllum bulbosum*), water
mint (*Mentha aquatica*), alexanders
(*Smyrnium olusatrum*), lily (*Lilium
candidum*), spurge (*Euphorbia* sp.),
f27r.

Apuleius Platonicus *Herbarium, MS.
Harley 5294,* 'Sanguinaria' and a man
being bitten by a dog, f25r.

GRECIS DR · Batosidea ·
A lii · Cinofbatos ·
P rophete · Simrophu ·
A lii · Emaricanos ·
A lii · Emaideos ·
I tali · Sinix ·
R omani · Rubum uocant ·
A lii · Mora siluatica ·

Nascitur incampis & insepibus· · · · · · · D AVRIVM · · · · DOLOREM ·

* Herbe erusci qui masculus· ex · · · · · · · · · · · · · · · pressus mauriculis·
  e tepefactus · & stillatus · auriu · · · · · · · · · · · · · dolore liberat.
  & psanare · · · · · · · · · · dicimus·

Herba · · · · · · · · · erusci qui mas· uiiij · & mircę qui mas·
ide· VIIIj· mali · · · · · · · · · granati sicci cortices teres·
decoquant inse· · · · · · · · & cacesinas impingue· & cum
refrigidauerit · · · · · · · · fomentabis tibi sessu· hoc
pinduu faciens miri · · · · fice stringet· & sanat·
    D PROFLVVIVM · · · · · · · MVLIERIS· Herbas rusci
qui mas teneras ter septenas · · · · · decoquis maqua usq: ad
tertias & triduo ieiuno potu dab·ita. · · · · · · · ut cotidie rino

ues potione · · · · D CARDIACOS· Herba erusci folia · · pse ca
imponuntur & mamille sinistre dolore tollit. AD VSVS
GINGEBARV ET DOLORV VITIA· Herbę erusci caules teneros
mmmo decoquis & ipsu uinu more continebis·sume · · · · · · faciu· · · L D
VVE REMEDIV· herbe erusci folia arefianc · · · · inubri · · ca · · nere
in clurio facto· resilit in presente neuo. AD · · · VVLNERA RE · centia
Herbę erusci flos auc maros sine collecti · · ones apiculo · · sanat Adcdolo
mata· herba rubu mmmo decocta · · adtrtas coq: · · uinofouebis cdo
lonaca & omia urtia sedat. Morsv SERPENTIS SIPEDEOH·

XXXV

D ÉUUCIUM   DOLOREM ·

ḣerba crifion cũ   fua   radice fiquif
incollo eã fecũ   portauerit fuſ
penfam· fauceſ ei   num   quã dolebuit·

D INTERANEOꝶ   doloꝶ

ḣerba crifion tunſa   &   fucuſ eı ex pſ fuſ   & potu
datuſ· interaneoꝶ   doloꝶ   mire fanat·
Legaſ eã menfe madio   & iunio·

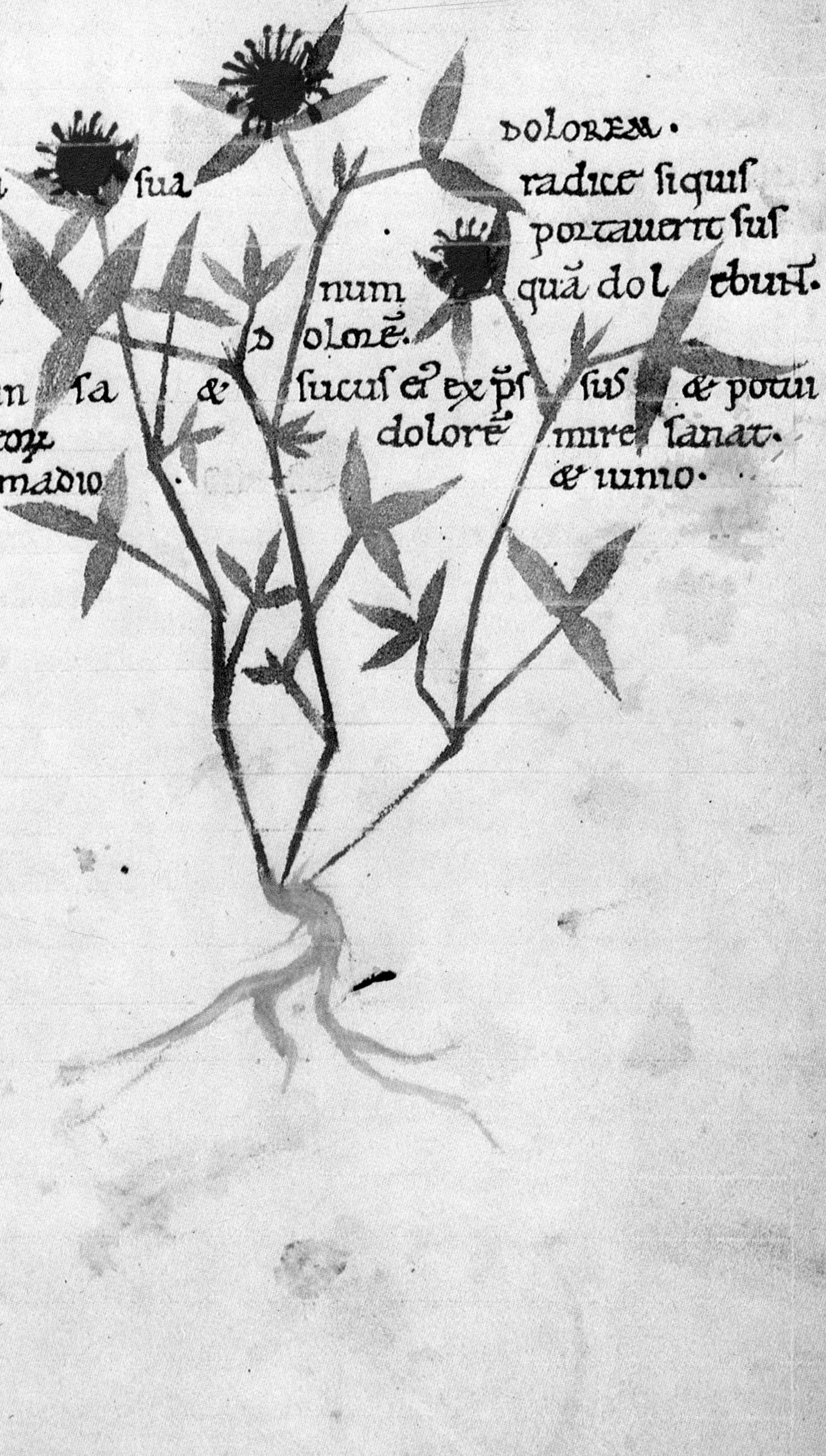

etiã uiulneribʒ impositę. eadẽ herba cũ aceto & oleorosatio
coc̃ta dolorẽ capitis mitigat. si caput exeadẽ coctione
foueat̃. qd́ etiã freneticis & letargis pdest· his q̃ sanguinẽ
uomunt puluerē ei ĩdragmis·IIII· id·ẽ·xij scrupuloscũ
uino accipe debent.

una spes
catapotia·I· ꝯ purge

·CRA·IIII·

Nascitur aspis   siue petrosis locis·
De una radice multi   rami· unũ cespitẽ tollens
breuis & minũta folis par   uissimis & incisis flore paruo
& rubello· naturę terminaci   ę· Eo tẽpore colligenda·ẽ
quo ẽ inseminĕ l̃ crudę sucus   ex p̃sius l̃ decoc̃te
sibibatᵘ pdẽ· l̃ diligent̃ mul̃   tria catapotia
q̃ ali quo ictu omenta uitia utriũc̃. tussientabʒ plenes durę
habentabʒ·l̃ qui urinã cũ dolore l̃ difficilt̃ emittunt· ydro
picis incipientabus p̃ menstrua quoq̃· euocant & fetus
matricũ· mortuũ plenũ quoq̃· morsibus adposita ea
dem herba siue cũ uino potata pdest· & iã mixta· cũ
mella uetent̃ ulcera purgat & sanat̃ tritę. & iã cum
oleo diligent̃ & oculis in posita caligñẽ detergit̃···

One of the most remarkable illustrated manuscripts of Apuleius is a codex written at the Abbey of Bury St Edmunds about the year AD 1120. Its imperfect Latin text is unimportant, and many of its figures are conventional; it is the surprising naturalism of a few of them that arouses our curiosity.

Three possible explanations have been suggested by Singer[1]: it could be that the naturalistic pictures were added to the manuscript at a later date; that these pictures are the only known survivors of a twelfth-century naturalistic school; or, simply, that the artist who produced them was far in advance of his time. The first of these can be ruled out since an examination of the manuscript shows that, exceptionally, the figures preceded the text. The second could in theory be true; but it seems less likely that the work of a whole school of illustrators should have been lost than that there was, as in the third hypothesis, a monk working in the early twelfth century who was both an artist and a true naturalist and who actually referred to living plants. Singer writes:

> We can reconstruct his method. He had before him a herbal of the usual Apuleius-Dioscorides type. He began by identifying the plants in his MS. with plants in the monastery garden. These he painted. Thus, for 'Viperiana' he adopted the milk thistle, *Carduus marianus*, then a garden plant from Southern Europe, where it is common in waste places, and now a weed of escape in Britain. Similarly, for 'Camedrium' of the ancient herbal he took *Teucrium chamaedrys*, another South European and West Asian form which, though now established in parts of this country, is unquestionably a garden escape . . . Finally, being unable to identify some of the figures in his original, he copied them.

Otto Pächt, however, in a most interesting article,[2] is not altogether sure that the entire credit for this naturalism can be given to the Bury St Edmunds herbal painter, considering it more probable that it was an 'archaising style' and that 'at least a part of the naturalistic elements of his plant pictures may have been taken over from an "Anglo-Saxon model" and so indirectly from the art of the Carolingian Renaissance'. Nonetheless, it was very fitting that this unusual codex should have been chosen by the Roxburghe Club for a facsimile edition, which was edited by Dr W. R. T. Gunther in 1925.

Of the plants here reproduced, clover and 'foxes glove' cannot be more precisely identified, but among the alternative names given to the latter is 'Apollinaris'. This stems from the legend that Apollo discovered the plant and gave it to Aesculapius. The herb and root of clover are said to be good for any internal pain, and the sap – if used in May or June – also 'heals marvellously'.

APULEIUS PLATONICUS
Herbarium
Bury St Edmunds, England, *c.* 1120
25.7 × 20 cm ($10\frac{1}{8}$ × $7\frac{7}{8}$ in)
108 folios
Bodleian Library, Oxford,
MS.Bodley 130
Colour plates p.34 Bramble (*Rubus fruticosus*), f26r; p.35 Clover (*Trifolium* sp.); f18r; p.38 'Foxes glove' (*Digitalis* sp.) and chamomile (*Chamaemelum nobile*), f44r.

1 Singer (1927), pp. 42–43.

2 Pächt (1950), p. 35 ff.

Opposite
Apuleius Platonicus *Herbarium, MS. Bodley 130*, Camedrium (*Teucrium chamaedrys*), f58v.

GRECIS dicitur foxes . gloue Decea .

A lii Striginō manicom .

A lii Dorignion .

A lii Cecalion .

J tali Apollinaris .

D aci herba uaccina .

A pollo hanc herbā dr̄ inuenisse.
& asclepio dedisse. unde nomen impo
suit ei apollinaris. D VVLNERA CIRONIA ET ARANEARV.

H erba apollinaris cū axungia uete sine sale teris & uinū
uetus sine fumo quatum unū axungia uetere. libere simul pis
sabis. & factū tam quā malagma & imponis sanabitur.

A lii	. partenicon	G alli	. Oblaodia .
A lii	D icolofam.	C ampani	. Obulatia .
P etosiris. T rocicoeliacos			
A lii	. A ptos . Omoeos.		A mula .
A lii	. Himpeos . Tusci .		Abiana .
O moeos	. J eroantemis. Daci .		A mulista .
A lii	. Aeliopteis .		Nascitur locis
J tali	. B ene olente.		cultis leges eā
A lii	. S upba		mse aprl
A lii	. A pirtos .		AD OCVLORV VITIA
A lii	. E liantes .		L dolores .
R omani.	B eneolente.		herbā camelon
A lii	. S upa		si qs ante solis
A lii	. S olisaciuū. meʒeþe.		ortū iuenerit.
E gypti.	T uorin . dicet ad al		bugine oculor. te carpeo.
	peto ut subuenias. & alligatā		secū portet incollo .

S i VOLVERIS SCIRE VIRTVTE ei? Facies eā inoleo q̄ndo sol ariete uenerit
  & egrū p

tollas. tecumq̃ deferas. & quamdiu
eam tecum portaueris: nichil mali
tibi euenerit. Nomen istius herbe:
Lupinum montanum.

Grecis dicitur: Termosorinos.
Nascitur autem secus sepes. uel in
locis sablosis. lupins mõ
tains.

573

Prima cura eius ad
lumbricos & tineas.
erbam lupinum monta
num cum aceti quidem cy
atho uno dabis bibere. sine mo
ra lumbricos & tineas eiciet.
74 ec autem eadem herba umbi
lico infantium trita sposita:
psectissime medetur. & psanat

575
Grecis sup... dis nuncupatur.
dem dicitur Cocosnidos. Quidã
uero Samellam eam uocant. u
pales. & panchenon. gypteis ue
ro: Vterym. tali: Crtocacim.
Quidam autem Latridem eam
appellant
erbe Latridis
granum cum poptime pur
gatum fuerit: in aqua calida po
tum dabis. statim alueum pur
gat. & eum sanat
577
herbe Lactuca Leporina dicit.
ascitur in locis cultis & sablosis.
epus autem in estate cum ani
mo desicit: hanc herbam come

nem. omniſq; durities ſoluunt. τ
ſpargunt. ꝯ

ꝯ Eadem ſtigmata corporum ſeptē
diebᵹ leuit infricata. ſine exulce
ratione detegunt. Eadem τ cum ſa
le poſita. τ inoze diutiuſ ſeruata.
appetitum edendi in omnibᵹ pſtāt.
Radix ipſiuſ. cum aceto trita. igné
ſacrum curat. Cum melle ut cum
oleo trita. contra morſum ſerpen
tium ꝓdeſt. Cum aqua. chyriadaſ
diſſoluit. Cum polenta. oclorum
dolorem ſedat. Preterea de cortice
radicis ipſiuſ. libre treſ τ ſex congia
uini dulciſ in amphoram mittun
tur τ reponuntur. ut ad medicine
uſum maturiſcat. τ ex eodem uino
chyatoſ treſ. τ unciaſ quatuor. aſ̄
miunciam dabiſ ad bibendum.

hiſ quorum corpᵃ ꝓꝑ curam ſecandū
eſt. ut hac potione ſoporati. doloze
ſecture ñ ſentiant. Mala autem ip
ſiuſ. ſiut olefriantur. ut edant. ſopo
rem. corporem cp ita ut uocem aufe
rant. faciunt. Succuſ quoꝗ ex cor
ticibᵹ radiciſ trite ex pſſuſ. in ua
ſe fictili poſituſ. in ſole. ut leni igni
culo coquat. aſſidue agitetur. donec
in melliſ graſſitudinem coactuſ.
prea in ſaluo loco. ad medicine u
ſum reponat. Radiceſ etiam ſicce
reſeruent. plibᵹ uſibᵹ ꝓ future. ad
feruoreſ ſcilicet ocloz. ad feruoreſ
uulnerum. ad duritiaſ τ collectioneſ
ſpargendaſ. ad ignem ſacrum ad
ſerpentiſ morſum. ad chyriadaſ τ ad
articulorum dolorem. Potio autē
huiuſ herbe accipitᷓ. ut qui ſecatur
non ſentiat dolorem. Nom̄ huiuſ
herbe. xvi. Thaſpiſ ſiue ana.

The Anglo-Norman Herbals

During the twelfth century the monastic centres in France and Germany exerted much less influence on English art than they had previously done, either before or after the Conquest. The Norman kings had renewed contact with their relations in Sicily, and the Crusades opened up the Near East to Constantinople and beyond. A new 'Romanesque' style evolved from these contacts with Byzantine art, one of whose characteristics was the use in manuscripts of a framed composition with painted or gilded background. Figures, when they occur, were treated three-dimensionally; but plants, now reduced to serving as decorations only, became virtually unrecognizable.

The following three Anglo-Norman manuscripts, all dating from the beginning of the thirteenth century, are illustrated in the Romanesque style. Considered as embellishments to the page, the paintings are charming; but to the would-be collector of herbs they are valueless, and since we have no need to make any practical use of them we may as well enjoy them. It is, however, interesting to note that at this very moment a Muslim botanist, Ibn al-Sūrī (1179–1242), was collecting plants in the Lebanon in the company of an artist who painted them as they were found, in various stages of growth.[1] Unfortunately his work has not survived.

Harley 1585 is in rather poor condition. The 'lupin' – possibly a species of *Coronilla* – and the unidentifiable umbellifer that accompanies it give a fair idea of the character of the illustrations, in which heavy outline is used to create a strong formal pattern. The text informs us that the lupin was 'placed upon the umbilical cord of infants', presumably to help to get rid of the cord.

Much more attractive are the pages of Sloane 1975, which are liberally embellished with gilding, while lettering has been picked out in blue, red and green to make the whole even more sumptuous. Most of the plants are enclosed by frames and stylized beyond recognition. The roots of the three artemisias shown have all been allowed to escape across the borders – a decorative device which was later to become common.

Opposite
Apuleius Platonicus *Herbarium, MS. Sloane 1975,* Mandrake (*Mandragora autumnalis*) and 'Thapsis' (perhaps hawkweed, *Hieracium* sp.).

1 G. Sarton, *Introduction to the History of Science,* vol. 2:54, 649; Baltimore, 1931.

APULEIUS PLATONICUS
Herbarium and other medical texts
England, *c.* 1200
21.3 × 15.2 cm (8⅜ × 6 in)
92 folios
British Library, London, MS.Harley 1585
Colour plate p. 39 'Lupin' (*Coronilla* sp.) and an umbellifer, f51v.

APULEIUS PLATONICUS
Herbarium and other medical texts
England, *c.* 1200
29.2 × 19.7 cm (11½ × 7¾ in)
95 folios
British Library, London, MS.Sloane 1975
Colour plates pp.42–43 Artemisias, ff16v–17r.

catrices. statim erimit eas. isimilem
corpi facit colorem. Nomisti herbe:
artemesia mono
glosos.

locis sablosis. ut montuosis. Prima cu
herbam arte   ra cu: ad iter facien
mesiam siquis iter faciens dum;
secum portauit: n sentiet itineris
laborem. fugat etiam demonia: in
domo posita. phibet mala medi
camta. auertit oclos maloru.   ad pe
erbam artemesiam   dum dolose.
contundas. cum auxungia: 7
imponas. pedum dolorem tollit ad
erbam arte   interanoru dolore;
mesiam tunsam inpuluerem
redactam. cum aqua mulsa potui
dabis. intestinoru dolorem mirifi
ce tollit. 7 diuisis infirmitatib; hoc
etiam siceceris: subuenit. Dom libe:
artemisia tagantes;

Amoeos: caristellum uocant. Alij:
toxotes. Alij: Ephesiam dicunt Alij:
aristolochiam Alij: Partenicon Alij:
apollitos, Alij: lysimachim: arteme
siam uocitant. Alij: sozusam Alij:
lysoprax. Prophe: eantropum Alij:
ceetesiam Alij: omeantisirisam Alij:
theonissis. Alij: Bubastes. Alij: ostan
tropu, Alij: emeronum Alij: Geno
sefestus Alij: Phylacterion. megam
Piragoras: fexasam. Egypti: alsaba
sar. Alij: toxobubz dicunt. Nascit

A moeos. crisantemis uocant egyp
tij: hym. Romani: tanntum uocat.
Alij: tanacitan. Alij: tanacipan.
Pma cura ei siquis febribz uexat.
erbe artemesie tagantes suc
cum cum oleo roseo pungef.
febres statim tollit. Ad uesice dolo
erbe arteme rem istrangui
sie tagantes. ex succo riam.
scripula duo. uini cyatum unu.
dabis bibere. n febricitanti. febri
citantiu: in aqua calida cyathos
duos. et remedium erit. Ad cora
erbam arteme rum dolorem.
siam tagantum tundis cum
axungia. et aceto. subigis et ponis.
et ligabis. tcia die sine aliqua dif
ficultate sanabit. Ad neruoy do
erbam artemesi lorem
am tagantem cum oleo be
ne subactam imponis mirifice
sanat. A pedum dolorem siquis g
erbe arteme uit uexatur
sie radicem cum melle dabis
manducare. pt cenam. liberabi
tur. ut uix credi possit. tantam
hre uirtutem. Vt infante hilare
erbam artemesi sanat
am incende. et subfumigabis
infantem. omis incursiones auer
tat. Nom istius hebr: Artemesia.
leptafilos uirtutes plures habet

Herba ista nascit circa fossas. ut
circa sepes. ut aggeres. flores es. ut
folia ipsius. si contriueris: sambuci
odorem hnt. Ad stomachi dolorem.
erbam artemesiam leptafillu
tunsam cum oleo amigdalino be
ne subactam more malagmatis. indu
cis in panno mundo. et linies. qnto die
sanabit. et si fuit ei artemesie radix su
plum edifitiu suspensa: domui nemo
nocebit.

erbe arteme Ad neruoy dolore.
sie leptafillis succum cum oleo
rosatio mixtum: punges eos. desinit
dolor. et tumor. et oie uitium tollit.
Nam has tres artemesias: diana dicit
inuenisse. uirtutes earu. et medicam
ta. chyroni centauro tradidit. q pmi
de his herbis medicinam instituit.
has autem herbas. ex nomine diane

dicunt Pytagore. Crisipicum. Ta
lj. verminaciam uocāt. Alij. luci
niam. Alij. lustrago. a peram.
Cotumbinam appellant. Alij. milita
riam. Alij. Veracpedium. nuncupāt
Nascitur ubiqȝ. in planis. y in aquosi
locis.

Prima uircus ad uulnera.
y puuocidas.
erbe verminacie
radix. in collo ligata. mirifice fa
cit. Ad strumas y puuocidas.
ertu verminacia trita cū axū
gia sine sale imposita mirifice fa
nit. ad eos qui induricias uenas habent.
y cibos non accipiunt.

erbe verminacie sucus dā bibe
cum uino. y melle. y aqua. y bē
liat. y sic bibat. statim sanabitur. A
ertu verminacia capuis dolore
solstacio lecta. y in pulirem redacta
igne robusto. dabis coclearia quinqȝ.
ex uino quam optimo cyacis tribus
potui sumpta. mirifice creditur pro
ficere. y ceteris pro cuiqȝ uiribȝ sic da
bis. Ad calculosos sanandos.
erbe verminacie radix contusa
cum mulso optimo tepido data.
credibiliter calculosis succurrit. si y
quicquid ē uidetur quod urinā impe
dit ad trahendum celerit producit.
erbe verminacie Ad capitis dolore
corona facta. in capite imposita
dolore capitis tollit. Ad serpentis morsū.
ertum verminacia cum folijs suis
y radicibus quisquis omultam.
eniecamqȝ secum portauerit. ab oibȝ
serpentibȝ tutus erit.

Ad percussum aranearum quas greci
spalangiones dicunt.
erbe verminacie fasciculum in uino
decoctum. ante trita. potui data. uel ei

There is a third Anglo-Norman manuscript which also uses the frame motif but, interestingly, includes several mythological figures. Normally medieval herbal illustrations, with the exception of the mandrake and a few others in which the discovery or virtue of a plant is described in anecdotal form, are confined to the representation of the plant only. We have already discussed the illustration for the herb 'Sanguinaria' of a man being bitten by a mad dog, which appears both in Harley 5294 and a related southern Italian manuscript, written in Beneventan script and now in Turin. We also know that two Greek manuscripts of Dioscorides, in the Bibliothèque Nationale in Paris (MS. Grec 2179)[1] and in the Lavra monastery on Mount Athos, both contain scenes illustrating herb gathering. This suggests a common ancestry with a Greek Dioscorides that included figures.

A fine page from Ashmole 1462 shows a centaur brandishing a plant said to represent centaury – 'Centauria major'; but one's heart goes out to any herb-gatherer who attempted to make use of it for purposes of identification. On the same page are two other plants, one of which – an asphodel – does show leaves that faintly resemble those of the genus *Asphodelus*, so common in Mediterranean countries; the other – 'Lappacium' – is perhaps some kind of sorrel (*Rumex* sp.). We also reproduce 'Mercury bringing the herb "Immolum" to Homer' – a page as delightful and as unhelpful as most of its companions. In both these the crudely modelled figures have been set against a red painted background outlined with gold, the border of the centaury picture being dramatically pierced by the plant.

The text of this manuscript is a mixture of medical and herbal bits and pieces, including some Apuleius and parts of Antonius Musa's treatise on botany.

APULEIUS PLATONICUS
Herbarium and other texts
England, *c.* 1200
30.5 × 19.5 cm (12 × 7¾ in)
82 folios
Bodleian Library, Oxford,
MS. Ashmole 1462
Colour plates p.46 'Gallitrichum',
'Immolum' and Homer, Mercury and
'Immolum' (perhaps houseleek,
Sempervivum tectorum), f26v; p.47
'Affodille' (asphodel, *Asphodelus*
sp.), 'Lappacium acutum' (sorrel,
Rumex acetosa) and a Centaur
holding 'Centauria' (perhaps
Centaurium sp.), f23r.
1 See p. 24 and colour plate p. 26.

Opposite
Apuleius Platonicus *Herbarium, MS.
Ashmole 1462*, Vervain (*Verbena
officinalis*) and a man stabbing a
serpent, f15v.

45

Prima cura est ad fistulas.

Herbe Extrifion de radice uncias
vi. Amuli uncias vi. Aceti cyathos duos. de adipe uulpis uncias tres
y in panno lineo. y impones. mirabere
effectum bonum. Cont̃ capitis fracta.

Herbe Extrifion superior pars sicca
y bene trita. equis ponderibz mi-
xta. y capiti fracto apposita. de eo ossa
fracta extrahit. aut siquid in corpore so-
poratum fuit. uel si pedibz calcata sint
ossa alicui serpentis. eadem herba contra omnia uenena ualet. Nom̃ istĩ herbe Galltericu aliud.

Prima   cura
ipsius   ad strumas urginum   ginum.

Herba Galltericum p se diligenter
trita. strumisqz urginum inpo-
sita. eas pfectissime sanat. Ad capillos

Herba Galltericum ita. unungendos.
y cum oleo bene decocta. omnisqz
corinis cum ea mixtis. pungas capil-
li nigri efficiuntur. si frequenti linie-
ris.   Nom̃ huĩ
                                herbe
                                Immo-
                                luoj.

Hec herba Immolum clarissima
Dominũ ꝫ herbarum. homero at-
testante. y inuentore ipsius mercurio
assignante. que iussu cum beneficio de-
monstratur. rotunda radice. in̄ graq̃
in magnitudine cepe est. Ad dolorem
Herba Immolum con   cyatricis.
tusa. y imposita. dolorem matcis
pfectissime sanat.

Homerus.   Mercurius.
         ductor.

                                Nom̃ istĩ herbe
                                Eleotropion. Duas
cyarimas uirtutes habet.

Agreis dicitur Ctoron. Alij. Dia-
liron. Alij. Scorpion. Alij. Eracleã
uocant. Alij. Crotoseron. y rophẽ
autẽ. Cinatres. Galli. Vrascorpion.
Pytagoras. Hisene. Egyptij. Ver-
tamnũ. Itali. ocyuloctiam eã dicunt.
Nascitur ubiqz locis cultis. y inultis.

Centū capitea . angl' affodille .

l'affodille

Herbe aſpodili ſuco cum oleo amig
dalino perungas . omnē dolorem
qui fuit in corpore mirifice ſanat .

Ad iecoris . uel epatis dolorē .
l'affodill
Herbe aſpodili radiculaſ decoques
cum aquā mulſata . potata uero
iecoris uel epatis dolorem mirifice tol
lit . Hom iſtē herbe : Orilapatruoz . Lapacioū
acutū .

Itali uocant eam . Lapacium acutū .
Romani : Rumice Alij : Idiam .
Alij : Rumiz cantarcam Egypti :

Semem dicunt . Naſcitur inter ſegete
uel ubiqz . Prima cura eius ſi qua duricia
herbā eſt in corpore naſcetur .

Lapacium acutū cum axungia ue
teri . J pane domeſtico capieſ . J inde ma
lagma facieſ . quaſi malagma . J impo
neſ . perfectiſſime ſanat . Hom iſtius
herbe Centauria maior . h   Anglice
huius genera ſunt duo .   Centorie
haſ autem centauriaſ
duaſ chirocentauroſ di
citur inueniſſe . inde ex
nomine ipſius centau
ri nomen eis ipoſuit .
Ipſe uero : de hiſ herbiſ
herbiſ medicinā inſtru
it . primiſqz egrota
tibus tradidit .

Quidam uocant eam . charonion
Alij : pletoniam .   unici : Abuſti
ſim . Alij : lumniteoz .   rophete : G
meracleoz . Alij : Cyronias dicunt .
Alij : Apogiriſiam Alij : polidiṁ .
Alij : Emereoſ . Egypti : Antauā .

lupinu montana

cu & q diu cu tecu port
tus nichil mali i occret.
cat au camelcon ppi sol
uarietati. De herba lup
inum montanum.
Dec agest uocat thermosc
quos nascet niarta sepes au
eis sablosis. ad lumbrice
occidat. Herba lupi
montanu ure cu radice &
ex aceto ciatu unu bibe sin
gra eiecet lrc insanti cu absi
itu in ubilico iponit. Ro d
Greci Lacirudos latini
creuocatu. Lacirudis urso cu
tali roboris digitalis manus cui insu
tate furce atqz solia alia longa alia ut a
locia semine isumitate ram & tquono & uer
rorundo ut apparis iq ia semina obiecta solus abinucie
runt rotunda a abheruo maiora q despgata spolus deposi
alba reptiut e dulcia. ad durici uentris cibelach
sem q e gnu dabis caro pgata gna vun
cta porui iaq singula vmox aluu cenia
Dascit locis cultis & sablosis lep cu estate
anuio dcie estu hac herba remediat idea
lactuca leporina dicit ad febricitantes.
Herba lactuca leporina sub posita sub pului
no nescienti remediabit. Si pili oculis obstant.
Herba leporina lactuca pilos sume religat. Rota
cucumeris.

Left
Apuleius Platonicus *Herbarium*, Eton, *MS. 204*, lefthand page, 'Lupinum montanum', and 'Lacteris', righthand page, 'Cucumis' and 'Cannabis', ff46v–47r.

APULEIUS PLATONICUS
Herbarium
Germany, *c.* 1200
29 × 19 cm ($11\frac{1}{2} \times 7\frac{1}{2}$ in)
80 folios
Eton College Library, Windsor, MS.204
Colour plates pp.50–51 Rhizotomists gathering herbs (left), Physician weighing drugs (right); p.54 Madonna lily (*Lilium candidum*) and other plants, f45r; p.55 Fern and saxifrage, f42r.

The Eton herbal, which again combines elements of Apuleius and Dioscorides, was written in Germany at the beginning of the thirteenth century. It opens with a splendid double-page: on the left a physician is seen directing his servants in the gathering of herbs, while on the right he supervises an assistant who is weighing drugs. There follow paintings of plants, and finally a bestiary (including a glorious blue elephant) by a different hand. As in the Anglo-Norman manuscripts, most of the plants are too stylized to be recognizable; but on one page a Madonna lily, though very stylized, is easily identifiable.

This manuscript is closely related to a manuscript of similar date and style, also German, now in the British Library, London (Harley 4986), and a resemblance, both as regards text and the choice of figures, to the already mentioned English herbal Ashmole 1431 (see p. 33) is also inescapable.

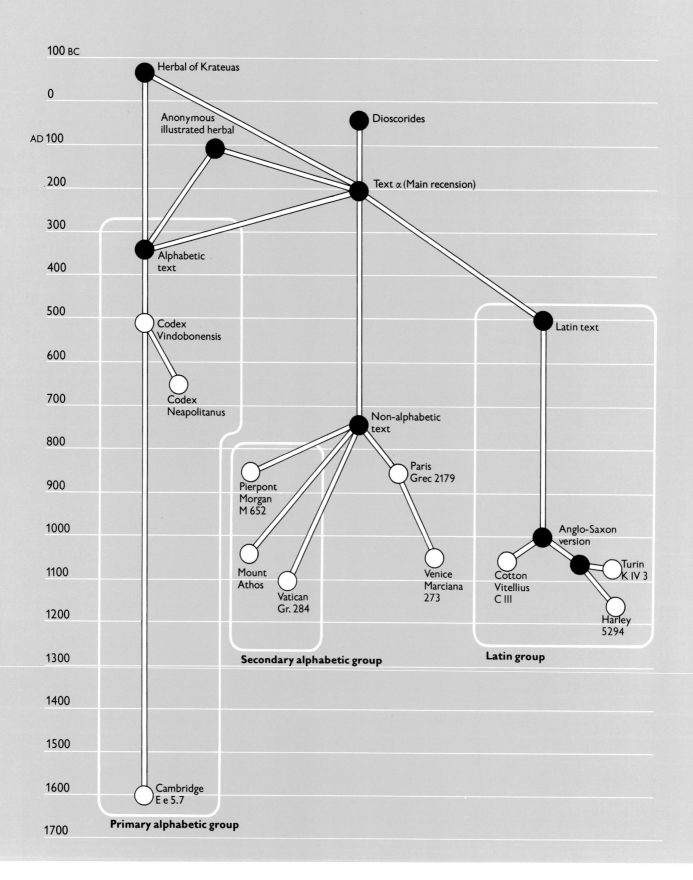

100 BC

Herbal of Krateuas

0

Anonymous
illustrated herbal

Dioscorides

AD 100

200

Text α (Main recension)

300

Alphabetic
text

400

500

Codex
Vindobonensis

Latin text

600

700

Codex
Neapolitanus

800

Non-alphabetic
text

900

Pierpont
Morgan
M 652

Paris
Grec 2179

1000

Anglo-Saxon
version

1100

Mount
Athos

Venice
Marciana
273

Cotton
Vitellius
C III

Turin
K IV 3

Vatican
Gr. 284

1200

Harley
5294

1300

Secondary alphabetic group

Latin group

1400

1500

1600

Cambridge
E e 5.7

1700

Primary alphabetic group

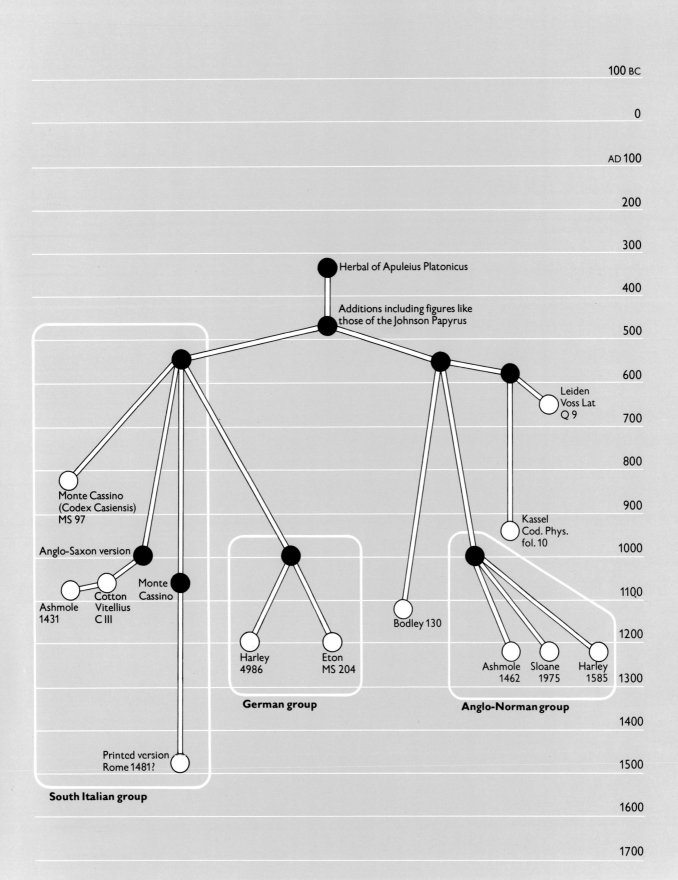

100 BC

0

AD 100

200

300

Herbal of Apuleius Platonicus

400

Additions including figures like
those of the Johnson Papyrus

500

600

Leiden
Voss Lat
Q 9

700

800

Monte Cassino
(Codex Casiensis)
MS 97

900

Kassel
Cod. Phys.
fol. 10

1000

Anglo-Saxon version

Monte
Cassino

1100

Ashmole
1431

Cotton
Vitellius
C III

Bodley 130

1200

Harley
4986

Eton
MS 204

Ashmole
1462

Sloane
1975

Harley
1585

1300

German group

Anglo-Norman group

1400

Printed version
Rome 1481?

1500

South Italian group

1600

1700

Opposite and above
The two charts, based on those of
Charles Singer, serve to give some
idea of the wealth of manuscripts of
Dioscorides and Apuleius Platonicus
that have survived. The lefthand
chart traces the descent of the
various groups of Dioscorides

manuscripts from the lost originals of
Krateuas. The righthand chart shows
the relationship of the versions of
the *Herbarium* of Apuleius
Platonicus. On both charts the white
circles indicate existing manuscripts
and the black circles denote a
missing link in the chain.

Greci crinion vocant.
ad luxum.

Herbe lilu folia tunsa
ęimposita efficaciř
sanat. ysi humor sue
rīt sedat. ad pcussu
ra serpentis.

Herbe lilu bulbū ētiv
ęipotu dab ipsū etiā
bulbū tritū morsui adpo
ne sanabiř. Thytimalli spe
cies s. vii. quarū alia mascuł
siue charatias appellatur ł
amigdalo. ł copios cometes
pos ineronitis. alipos. Latini
nos arcos. alia femina siue mirthi
ttes. ł charittes. chametis carttis. roma
ni murtilago. tttimallū.

cometes. aut
eataeitis elos co
valteū. Pphe go

bracherur.

lilium.

capria. alia pa
ralos siue tyhi
mallos. peplish
thymallis para
plion. meronion.
Quarta elio scopos.
deittis. tythimallis
latini cicer. colūbinū
lse eapgine.
Quinta q̃ parisias. viden
tudes. vii. platisillos. siue

capillof veneris. Nasci̅ iaq̅fif
locif uirgultif nigs le̅ib̅ cu̅ſplen
do̅re bipalmif aut coriandru̅ ſciſ
ſiſ iſu̅mitate. ad cauculof.
herba̅ ſariſtraga̅ c̅tra eruino bibe̅
du̅ dato felicitanti eraq̅ calida p̅
ſenſ effect̅ ab er p̅tis t̅dit̅ ut eode̅
die pſactif eiectif q̅ cauculiſ ſa̅
effectuſ ſit.

ſarıſtraga

S.

Cauc

noïa hedere.

Greci cyſon. melan
crifoſ metaſ. ciſſi
on necion. Galli
Boluſ ſerron. Vaci
arborria. Latini
Hederam̅g. ad caucu
loſ depellendoſ.
herbe heſle bacaſ. vii. aut xii.
c̅taſ eraq̅ i̅potu ſumptaſ
mirt cauculoſ i̅ueſica e̅gre
gatoſ frangere & ext̅urbere
p̅ur̅nam c̅tum eſt.

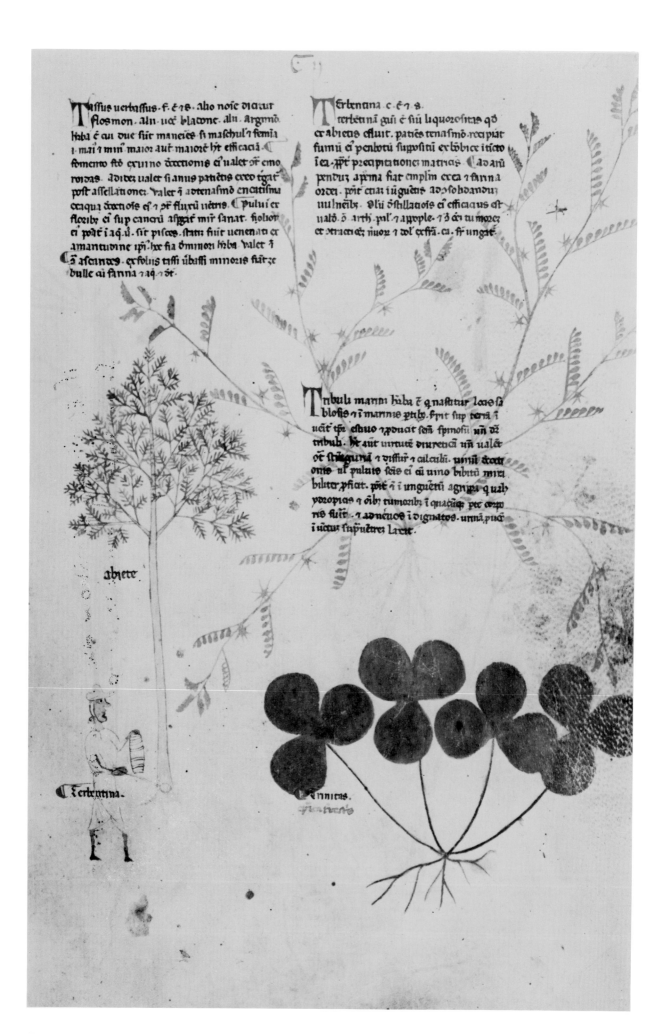

Tissus uerbassus. f. e 7 s. alio noie dicitur
flosmon. alii uoc blacone. alii argimo
hiba e cui due sit maneies. si maschul 7 femia
i mai 7 min maior aut maiore ht efficacia
fomento sto ex uino affectiones ei ualet of emo
roidas. adde ualet si anus patiens cero tegat
post assellatiões. ualet 7 ad tenasmo eneatisima
ceiqua affectiones es 7 of fluxu uentris. Puluis ex
floribz ei sup cancrū aspgat mir sanat. fioliox
ei podt i aq.u. sit pisces. statim sint uenenati er
amantudine ipi hec fia ō minor hiba. ualet 7
co ascanters. ex folus tissi ū bassi minoris fiat ze
bulle aū farina 7 aq. of.

Terbentina. c. e 7 s.
Terbētina gui e sui liquorositas qd
ex abietis effluit. patiēs tenasmō recipiat
fumū cu penlotu suppositi ex bobice i teio
i ea. xpt precipitatiões matricis. Ad aru
penduz apina fiat emplm crea 7 farina
orddi. pot etiam iu guētis ad psoluendum
uulneibz. Oliu stillatiois cu efficacius est
ualdo. co arth. pul. 7 appole. 7 ad cu tu moze
er straceos; nuon 7 dol exsia. cu. sr ungit.

Tribuli marini hiba e q nascitur locis sa
blosis 7 i marinis ptibz. sprit sup terra i
uesit tpe estiuo 7 producat sem spinosū un dr
tribuli. hc aut uirtute diuretica uū ualet
of straguriā 7 dissur 7 calculi. umili decoct
onis ul pulueris sciis ei aū uino bibitū miri
biliter psiat. pot 7 i unguētis agripa q uale
yoropicis 7 oibz tumoribz i gnaciuis pe corp
ris suit. 7 ad neruos i dignitos. urina puel
i uetus supuetris laxit.

abiete

Terbentina.

Tribulus.

56

The Rebirth of Naturalism

The steady decline in naturalism in botanical illustration continued virtually without interruption until almost the end of the fourteenth century. But already, though snow still lay upon the ground, there had come a century earlier the first signs that the long, cold winter of the Middle Ages was drawing to its close. Suddenly

> there was promise of spring in the air. The love-songs of the Troubadours, with their joy in birds and flowers, were echoed in Germany by the Minnesänger; in Assisi, St Francis praised God 'for our Sister, Mother Earth, who . . . bringeth forth divers fruit and bright flowers and herbs'; and the decade [the 1260s] which saw the birth of Dante and the writings of Albertus Magnus also witnessed the exquisite chiselled foliage upon the capitals of Rheims and Naumburg cathedrals. Gradually the dread of Nature was banished from men's minds; once again the world took pleasure in her meadows, her flowers, and the song of birds.[1]

But though St Francis sang of the beauty of flowers, his contemporary, Giotto, who painted birds and other animals with tolerable naturalism, still made trees like outsize herbs, and for much of the *trecento* almost the only recognizable flower in the paintings of Tuscan artists was the occasional Madonna lily. We must therefore now turn to southern Italy for the next stage in the development of botanical illustration.

As the abstract, stylized herbals of northern Europe moved further and further away from their original purpose – that of helping the doctor or herbalist to identify the plants for which he was searching – so, in southern Italy, at that time under Norman rule and in contact with Arabic science, there came the desire to revert to the making of herbals of practical value. At Salerno, near Naples, there had arisen towards the end of the eleventh century the first medical school in Europe,[2] whose leading figure was

Opposite
Liber de Simplici Medicina, MS. *Egerton 747*, 'Abiete' (a fir yielding turpentine), 'Tribuli marini' (caltrops, *Tribulus terrestris*) and 'Trinitas' (perhaps clover, *Trifolium* sp.), f102r.

1 Blunt (1950), p. 18.

2 After the foundation in 1224 by the Emperor Frederick II of a university in Naples, the medical school at Salerno (which had achieved university status in 1150) gradually waned in importance until its reputation for conferring 'bogus degrees' led to its official closure by Napoleon in 1811.

pia aquatica z terrestris.

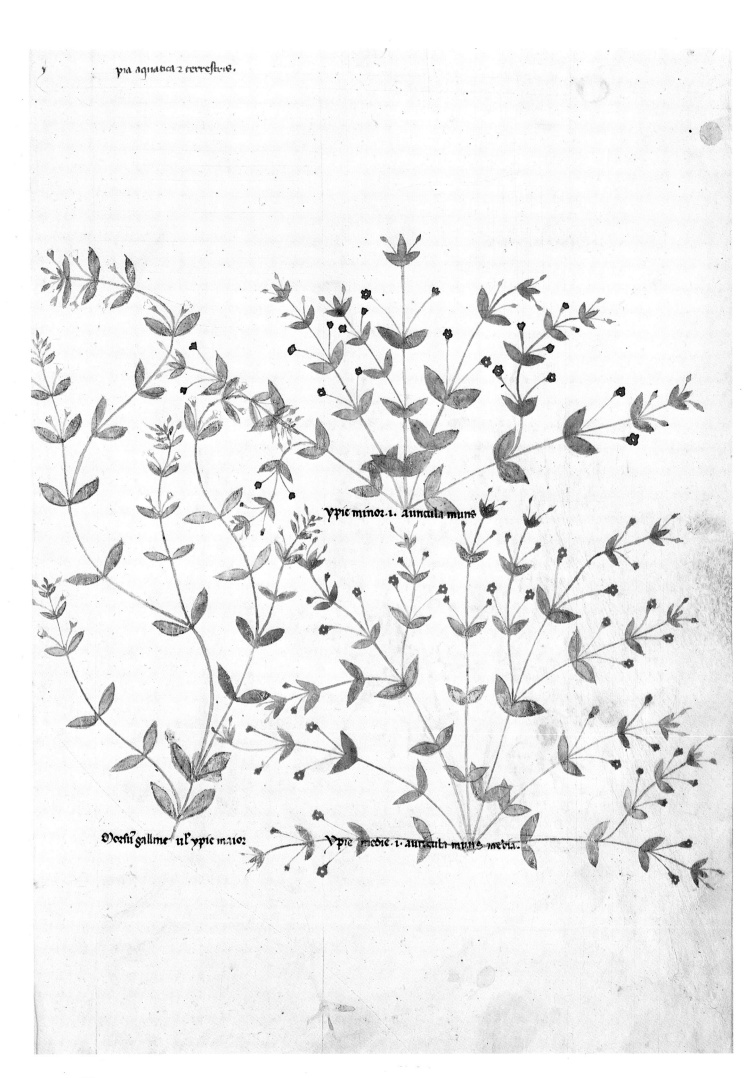

Ypie minor.i. auricula muris

Morsu galline ul ypie maior

Ypie medie.i.auricula muris media.

58

Bruſi ſiue bruſcus · es · cal·
ſic al · iij · gᵒ

Colloquintida · es · cal · iij · g
e ſeca al · ij · e es poma de ai
bie qui naix otra mar · e a vertut
deſolutina · e pinga malencolia
val ō dlor de las dens · et c̃ ·

Caſſia fiſtula · es · cal · e hu · tem
pate · e es fruit dalbre · e ſi no
las caſſafiſtula en recepta · deues
metre la meſola · val apurgar lo
ventre · e mundifica lo ſanc · ꝛ c̃ ·

Cuſcuta · es · cal · i · gᵒ · e ſeca
al · ij · pot ſe gardar per · ij · ans
e pinga flema e malencolia · e es
bona contra eſtranguria · et · c̃ ·

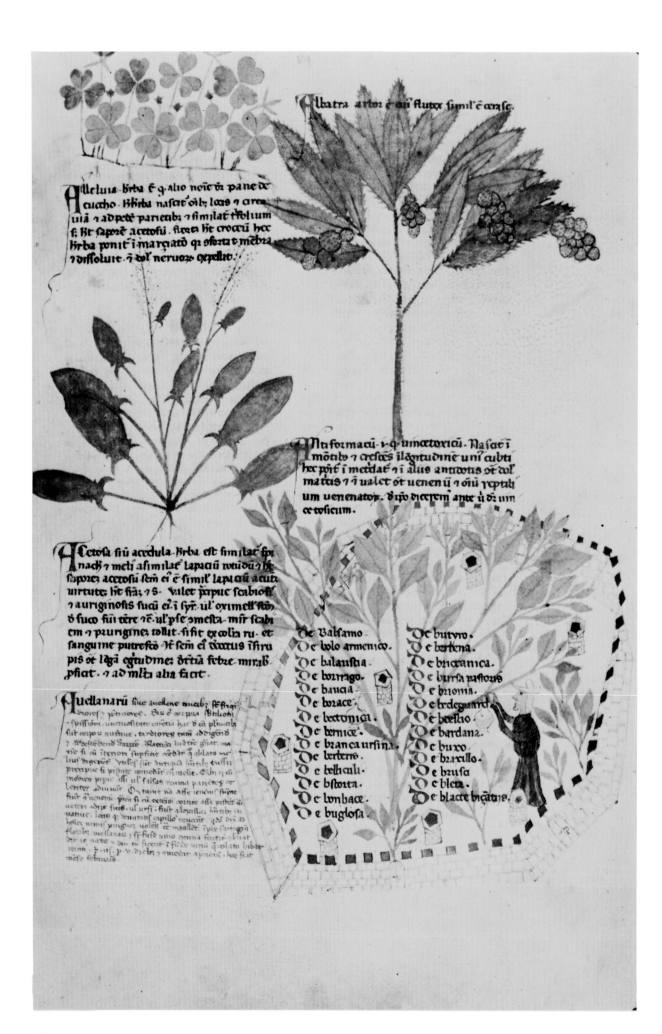

Albatra arbor e cui flux simil e cerase.

Alleluia herba e q alio noie tu pane de
cuccho. Herba nascit oib; locis 7 circa
uia 7 ad petu parietibz 7 similat trifolium
s. Et sapore acctosu. flores ht croceu hec
herba ponit i marciato qz ofortat mebra
7 dissoluit. 7 dol neruor expellit.

Anti formacu. i. q uincetoxicu. Nascit i
motibz 7 crescit i logitudine uni cubti
hec pot i meridiat 7 i aliis antidotis et dol
matis 7 n ualet ot uenen u 7 oiu reptali
um uenenator. Sicp diceren ante u dr ceu
ce tosicum.

Acetosa siu acedula herba est similat spi
nach 7 meli asimilat lapaciu rotudu 7 hi
sapore acctosu sem e e simil lapaciu acuti
uirtute ht fria; 7 s. ualet ppue scabiosi
7 auriginosis fucu ei i syr ul oximell ide
o suco sui tere re ul ipse omesta mir scabi
em 7 pruriginem tollit sifit excolia ru et
sanguine putrefco sse sem e oortus istiru
pis ot laga egitudine ortia febre mirabl
pfiat. 7 ad mlta alia facit.

Auellanaru siue auellane mucabz sefrigi
diores 7 pinateores. Sin e corpor hetior
pissione unctuositate onfcta hic o eu pinah
sut corpora nutriue. tardiores tm adigend
7 officedendi stages. Masenia lucere giet. me
rie si eu iteron superficie uerdr q ablato me
lius digerur. ualet siu antiqua hutilz tussi
precipue si pisate comedat cu melle. Obri eu
modico piper aspi ul falsato reuma panereos er
leniter adiuuat. Oz tame na asse teduns stipe
siut a ueneni ppia si cu cetteior cornie asse pister au
ueteri adipe suis. ul ursi siue allopticia hubitr cu
nature. loca qz denutiur capillo reuocat. qui dix as
hoies nimis pingue uoles ot maalte ipse stringen
floribz auellanar. 7 si fuld uino omnia fortir obliat
de se nocte 7 diu eu sicent i fide uinu ocolata bibati
leun. 5. iii. p. u. diebz 7 comedat apnoctu. hec fiat
mese februaio.

De Balsamo
De bolo armenico.
De bilaustia.
De borrago.
De baucia.
De borace.
De bectonica.
De bernice.
De branca ursina.
De berteris.
De belliculi.
De bistorta.
De bonbace.
De buglosa.

De butyro.
De bertena.
De brutanica.
De bursa pastoris.
De brionia.
De brdegnand.
De beretlio.
De bardana.
De buxo.
De braxillo.
De brusa.
De blera.
De blacte bizatus.

subsequently to be a certain Johannes (?) Platearius, compiler in the thirteenth century of an influential work entitled by its author *Liber de Simplici Medicina*, but more commonly known by its opening words, 'Circa Instans'. It drew not only on the usual Latin material but on Arabic sources.

The *Liber de Simplici Medicina* could perhaps best be described as the first dictionary of drug synonyms. The British Library possesses the earliest surviving illustrated manuscript of this text that we know of, *Tractatus de Herbis*, written in the early fourteenth century. If we accept Otto Pächt's verdict on Bodley 130, and unless any marginally earlier manuscript similar to Egerton 747 has been lost, the latter marks a new departure in the history of herbal illustration. Pächt, writing of Egerton 747, maintains that simultaneously with the search for trustworthy models to copy, sometimes perhaps in Arabic versions of Dioscorides,

> herbal illustrators [now] began to correct the transmitted plant pictures by consulting nature wherever possible and that meant in the first place that one started to make full use of the local flora. . . . A new critical spirit becomes manifest in their work and a new courage to explore the visual world and to find out things for themselves. The *Secreta Salernitana*[1] pictures as represented by Egerton MS. 747 cannot yet be counted as portraits in the full sense of the word; they are not based on studies drawn exclusively from life, but are rather the result of a careful comparison between painted models (of classical origin) and life models. [2]

Detail is minutely observed; but it is often used piecemeal and two-dimensionally, thus, for example, making a pine tree look like a single branch or a love-in-a-mist as flat as a herbarium specimen. It was to take almost another hundred years before we come to botanical illustrations that can really stand comparison with those in the *Codex Vindobonensis*.

However, in addition to its delicate if artificial botanical drawings, Egerton 747 contains a number of small landscape scenes with figures illustrating how the plants were gathered. Thus under balsam we find a man collecting resin from a large tree in an enclosed garden. They are simple scenes, very different from the stylized herb-gathering depicted in the Eton manuscript, which were to point the way for a new generation of herbal illustrators who were soon to develop and expand the landscape theme.

A Hispano-Provençal herbal provides the next link in the chain. The text is an abbreviated version of that of the *Secreta Salernitana* compendium as we know it from Egerton 747. The manuscripts start in the same sequence and the illustrations cover much the same subjects; but emphasis has moved from the appearance of the plants to scenes showing their medicinal virtues and the customs and occupations associated with them in everyday life. Most of these paintings include figures or animals.

Liber de Simplici Medicina
Salerno, early fourteenth century
34.9×24.7 cm ($13\frac{3}{4} \times 9\frac{3}{4}$ in)
147 folios
British Library, London,
MS.Egerton 747
Colour plate p.58 Pimpernels
(*Anagallis* sp.), f107r.

1 Another name for the *Liber de Simplici Medicina*.

2 Pächt (1950), p. 29, and see E. S. Rohde (1922), p. 193. A French version of Egerton 747, made in 1458, is in Modena (*Tractatus de Herbis*, MS 993).

Opposite
Liber de Simplici Medicina, MS. Egerton 747, 'Alleluia' (*Oxalis* sp.), 'Acetosa' (perhaps sorrel, *Rumex acetosa*), 'Albatra' (strawberry-tree, *Arbutus unedo*) and 'Balsamo' (balsam tree), f12r.

Secreta Salernitana
Spain or Provence, mid-fourteenth century
Biblioteca Nazionale Centrale,
Florence, MS.Cod.Pal.586
Colour plate p.59 Butcher's broom (*Ruscus aculeatus*), bitter apple (*Citrullus colocynthis*), cassia (*Cassia senna*) and dodder (*Cuscuta* sp.), f17r.

Porri. ꝯplo. ca. iii̾. ſic m̾. Electio napﬆa. i. montani acuti. uiuani tum. puꝛeant urinaꝛ. ad
uit incoꝛtu. ꞇ cū melle mūdificat pect ꞇ catarꝛis/ noæumtum cereb̾roꝛ ſenſib︖ Remo noℓℓ
eū olo ſiſamio aut amigdalaꝛ dulciū. Quid gn̄ant ſanguinē ad uſℓℓ ꞇ coleā acuta︖ ꝯueit
mag. fris. ſeneċtuti hyeme ſeptentrionalib︖

NAture f. & h. ī 2̄ . Meliuſ ex eiſ dulceſ aquo
nſi. Iuuamentum in egritudinibus . Nocumentū
digeſtioni . Remotio nocumenti cum penidiſ ɛucha
riniſ .

IBN BOTLÂN *Tacuinum Sanitatis*
(Tables of Health)
Po Valley, *c.* 1380
Bibliothèque Nationale, Paris,
MS.Lat.Nouv.Acq.1673

IBN BOTLÂN *Tacuinum Sanitatis*
Po Valley, *c.* 1380–1400
Université de Liège, MS.1041

IBN BOTLÂN *Tacuinum Sanitatis*
Po Valley, *c.* 1380–1400
33.2 × 23 cm (13 × 9 in)
112 folios
Österreichische Nationalbibliothek,
Vienna, MS.Series Nova 2644
Colour plate p.62 Leeks (*Allium*
porrum), f25r.

Theatrum Sanitatis
Po Valley, *c.* 1380–1400
Biblioteca Casanatense, Rome,
MS.4182

IBN BOTLÂN *Tacuinum Sanitatis*
Po Valley, *c.* 1400
Bibliothèque Municipale, Rouen,
MS.Leber, 1088
Colour plate p.63 Melons (*Cucumis*
melo), f19r.

1 See Cogliati Arano (1976).
2 A facsimile was published by La
Libreria dello Stato, Rome, in 1944.

3 Cogliati Arano (1976), p. 6.

Towards the end of the fourteenth century, probably around the year 1380, we encounter the first of a group of north Italian manuscripts which, though herbals in part only, also herald this fresh approach to the representation of plants. The work in question is entitled *Tacuinum Sanitatis*,[1] and is a medical handbook to the art of leading a healthy life.

The word *tacuinum* is said to be derived from the Arabic *taqwîm*, 'tables' (i.e. arranged in tabular form), and the author was probably an Arabian physician known by innumerable names of which Ibn Botlân, the most compact, is now the most conveniently used when referring to him. He seems to have been a Baghdadi who subsequently practised in Mosul, Diyarbakir, Egypt and Constantinople, and finally retired to a monastery in Antioch, where he died in 1086. It is known that the text had been translated into Latin by at least as early as 1266, and many manuscripts of his vade-mecum, both in Arabic and in Latin, still exist. Of the latter, the five listed here are fully illustrated. The manuscript in the Casanatense Library in Rome is actually entitled *Theatrum Sanitatis*,[2] and Pächt believes it to be a Salernitan work illustrated in the style of the other *Tacuina*.

In the Rouen manuscript the author defines the purpose of his book as follows:

> The *Tacuinum Sanitatis* is about the six things that are necessary for every man in the daily preservation of his health, about their correct uses and their effects. The first is the treatment of air, which concerns the heart. The second is the correct use of foods and drinks. The third is the correct use of movement and rest. The fourth is the problem of prohibition of the body from sleep, or excessive wakefulness. The fifth is the correct use of elimination and retention of humours. The sixth is the regulating of the person by moderating joy, anger, fear and distress. The secret of the preservation of health, in fact, will be in the proper balance of all these elements, since it is the disturbance of this balance that causes illnesses which the glorious and most exalted God permits.[3]

It is, of course, with the second of these, which deals with the value of plants as food or as medicine, that we are here principally concerned.

Most of the illustrations contain figures, but there are a few – for example, that of the 'Indus or Palestinian Melons' in the Rouen manuscript – that, even if derivative, are botanical drawings in the ordinarily accepted sense. Each bears a text giving instructions for the use of the plant, a warning of its possible ill effects, and so on. The melon is inscribed:

> *Nature:* Cold and humid in the second degree. *Optimum:* Those that are sweet and watery. *Usefulness:* Good in illnesses. *Dangers:* Bad for the Digestion. *Neutralization of the Dangers:* With barley-sugar.

Of the leeks in the Vienna manuscript, the author writes:

> They stimulate urination, influence coitus and, mixed with honey, clear up catarrh of the chest. . . . They cause hot blood and acute crisis of the bile. They are primarily

Itue r ominatur omnia nom??a poetaru psita in libro hic Et
??ignat. p ?nam prim??n ??eram ipius nominis h??.

Ibn Botlân *Tacuinum Sanitatis, MS.
1041*, Ibn Botlân writing his
Tacuinum Sanitatis, f lv.

indicated for cold temperaments, for old people, in Winter,
and in the Northerly regions.[1]

1 Cogliati Arano (1976) plates XXI
and XXVIII.

All five manuscripts contain a portrait of the author. In the Liège
copy he sits alone in a pleasantly cluttered scriptorium,
displaying his book which is inscribed: 'Albullasem de Baldac
[one of his many names], son of Habdi the Physician, composed
this book.' Below is a list of the abbreviations he proposes to use
for the authorities he quotes. This drawing is uncoloured. In two
of the others (Rome and Paris) he is also seen alone in his study; in
the Rouen manuscript he is shown instructing a pupil, and in that
at Vienna two are arriving for their tutorial.

The illustrations in all of these manuscripts are probably
related to the studio of Giovannino de' Grassi (d. 1398), who had
first set up shop in Milan around the year 1370 and was to have a
great influence on the so-called 'International Gothic' style. They
have that wonderful freshness which we associate with the
revival of naturalism as the Middle Ages drew to their close.

To take but a few of the joyful scenes depicted: a buxom girl
picks cabbages that would win a prize at any show; an elegant
youth has climbed a tree to pick cherries; another gathers
pomegranates as large as footballs. The inevitable mandrake is
there, head and shoulders above ground, together with the dog
chained to the plant, and its owner who averts his eyes. (Spread
on the skin the mandrake 'works against elephantiasis'.) A
damsel in courtly dress stands in a field of millet; she is far too
fine to reap the harvest herself, but a flock of birds is saving her
the trouble. Rue growing in a circular bed enclosed by a wattle
fence is being picked by an old man and his son.... The whole
world, which must in fact in those days have been very
uncomfortable, seems 'Paradise enow'.

e piu bumite cha la scorça la quale ha uirtu de incarnare le piage
e le ulceration. Le scorçe e le foie del pin macore e piu forte cha
del pin menore dicto. e lo fumo el quale se leua del legno del pin coa
molto a i pili de le coie che chaçe. e ala coroxion inlo cancon deli ogi i
uerso el naxo. e al corso de le lagreme de li ogi. Dice viascoride
che la scorça de lalbore del pin menore. e la scorça del pin maschio e stip
tice e coa a quili che ha male de punxi quando le se tria e po se spolue
rega souira el luego. E quando de questa scorça spoluerega se mesca cum
lo lutargiero çoe cum la spuma de laçento e cum el poluere de incen
so coa a la ulceration che uen inlo corpo. e ala scotaura del fugo. E i
quando questo poluere se confecta cum la ceta pesfata cum olio mir
cum a salda le ulceration che e inli corpi debele. E quando el se mesca
cum lo uruolo non laga crescere le ulceration che uene chiama forun
ge. e fasene suffumigation ala mare e chaçça fuora el fantolin e la secu
dina çoe un paniculo cosi chiama. E ha uertu de strençere el uentre e
de retignire la urina. E quando se tria la foia de questo arbore e fasene
empiastro mitiga i dolore de le aposteme e non lassa chel sangue desco
ra de le piage bumite. E quando lo se tria e cuorese cum lo aceo e po
fasene lauande coa al dolore de i dente. E quando sene beue la quanti
ta de   cum laqua ouere cum el miele coa ala passion del fico

notabile ochi

a i dolor di denti
alba.

Ce la uiola. Capitolo Crrrbj.

Dascorides dixe che la uiola e una herba cheha le foie menore chala
ellera e pia negre e no e molto differencie in figura. dale foie de
la uiola a quelle de la ellera. La gamba de la uiola esse fuora de
una raxer e soura questa gamba e pello e uiana e un fiore purpureo
de bon odore e nasce ingi luogi umbrosi e asperi. Gallieno dixe
che la substancia de questo foie e aquosa. La uertu. Prima de que
ste foie e uuocho frieda. La uertu segonda e che le e lautiue. La terça
uertu e che le mitiga le apostemaciom calde quando le se mette sole
soura quelle o cum farina de orço e coa ala infiarom che se fa in la bocca
del stomego. e ala infiarom de loto. Lo fiore so ha uertu de menare
fuora la collera e de mitigare eciandio le infiarom del stomego. Que
sta medesima sentencia conferma Brascorides e oltra ço el dixe che i
quando se fa empiastro cum queste foie sole e cum farina de orço me
scende quello empiastro coa al buello che uen fuora dal culo. E dixe chel
fiore so per la propriete che e in quelle coa ala squinancia e ala epillen
sia che uen apiuti quando el se beue cum laqua. La apropriete del fiore
Aben mesuer dixe chel fiore ha propriete de menare fuora la colle
ra de li intestim e del stomego e coa ala infiarom de quilli e al dolore de
la testa caldo e ala squinancia che uen apiuti quando el se rceue cum

 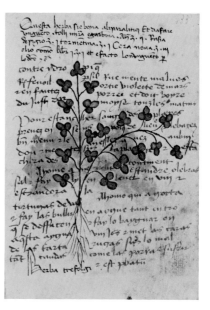

Far right
Herbal in Italian, Yale, *H 1–50*,
Clover (*Trifolium* sp.).

Right
Herbal in Italian, Yale, *H 1–50*,
Convolvulus sp.

Herbal in Italian
Italy, fourteenth century
20 × 15 cm (7⅞ × 5⅞ in)
50 folios of 152 in the volume
Medical Library, Yale University,
New Haven, H 1–50

1 See Blunt (1950), pp. 19–25. The
well-known botanical drawings of
Leonardo and Dürer date for the
most part from shortly before or
after the year 1500.

SERAPION THE YOUNGER
Herbolario volgare (Popular
Herbal)
Padua, 1390–1400
34.9 × 23.8 cm (13¾ × 9⅜ in)
289 folios
British Library, London,
MS.Egerton 2020
Colour plates p.66 Pine (*Pinus* sp.),
f46r; p.67 Violet (*Viola odorata*),
f94r; pp.70–71 Vine (*Vitis vinifera*),
ff27v–28r.

The Yale Medical Library possesses a manuscript which includes fifty leaves of a fourteenth-century herbal illustrated with sixteen paintings of plants. The remainder consists of a collection of medical recipes dating from the following century.

In the same library there is a herbal written in Lombardy about 1400. Its text is principally taken from Apuleius, but there is in addition material derived from Dioscorides and other classical authors. The manuscript contains six large miniatures and a number of smaller ones. We have not seen either of these works, the latter of which was bequeathed to Yale in 1937 by Dr Harvey Cushing and the former purchased in 1960.

Some of the most attractive representations of flowers made in the fifteenth century are to be found, not in herbals but in the borders of illuminated manuscripts, in the sketchbooks or individual studies of artists such as Pisanello, Jacopo Bellini, Leonardo da Vinci and Dürer, and in the religious paintings of Italian, Flemish and German artists; these, too, do not really concern us here.[1] There are, however, a number of important herbals of this century which deserve detailed consideration.

Probably the earliest and certainly the most remarkable of these is an Italian translation of a treatise on medical botany by the Arab physician Serapion the Younger (*c*. AD 800). The text was written by a Paduan monk, Jacopo Filippo, for Francesco Carrara the Younger, the last Lord of Padua, who was deposed in 1403 and strangled in a Venetian prison three years later. Space was left in the manuscript for a considerable number of illustrations of plants, only about fifty of which were ever executed. Most of these are highly naturalistic and beautifully painted in gouache on vellum, and many show an independent attitude on the part of the anonymous artist in rejecting the traditional representation in herbals of the entire plant. Indeed, it is precisely this naturalism and independence that arouses our suspicions. The script appropriately confirms a date of around 1390–1400; is it possible that the figures were added later?

The answer would appear to be, No. For a long time it was held that the far more substantial herbal of Benedetto Rinio, compiled in 1419 and to be discussed in a moment, was the first such work

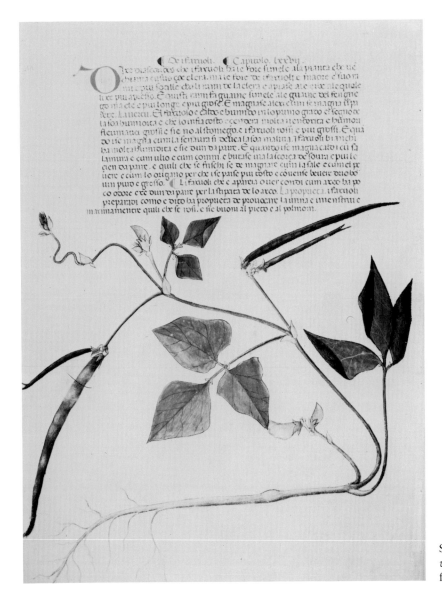

Serapion the Younger *Herbolario volgare, MS. Egerton 2020*, Bean, f56v.

since classical times to be illustrated with paintings made direct from nature; but Pächt[1] has demonstrated conclusively that twenty at least of the illustrations to Rinio are *directly copied* from those in Egerton 2020. This gives the anonymous artist of the latter work precedence, and thus in all probability a place of prime importance in the history of botanical illustration. Pächt continues:

> That the Carrara herbal was the first modern collection of naturalistic plant portraits ever made, we cannot take for granted, but there can hardly be any doubt that it represents the initial phase in nature studies, a kind of botanical counterpart to de' Grassi's animal sketchbook, and that it was the Paduan artist, whose name unfortunately we do not know, who had the courage to turn his back on all pattern books and to look nature straight in the face.

> Padua, with its famous university and medical faculty – the north Italian successor of Salerno and Naples – was a fitting place for this revolution to have occurred, and it was equally appropriate that the manuscript should later have passed into the possession of the celebrated Bolognese naturalist and founder of Padua's botanic garden, Ulisse Aldrovandi (1522–1605).

1 Pächt (1950), p. 30 ff.

69

rē muo de albo. E quando questa herba fioriffe se recoglie la so fiore e repo
nese in un vassello de terra senza in colaio cum aieo de to che e recta e
vestra unum pumo bianco e siccoa o un umbra. e nase a fa de questa in
una cona chiara obaca. La uertu de le fiore. de questa uigna e stipati
e perço quanto la se aue confota el stomego e prouoca la urina per i
che el strenge el uentre e strenge el fluxo del sangue. e çoa al stomego
defectuoso. in lo quale e el cibo coructo a corrupto. Questo fiore se me
sca cum sauar e cum lo ulio roxo e fasene biadeon al cauo al coloxe del
cauo. Ancora si se fa empiastro de questo fiore bianco e secco e çoa
ale apostemaçion. E quando questo fiore sebia e po se mescla cum el mie
le e cum el sofian e cum ulio e cum mirra e po fasene empiastro çoa ala
uigna che fa ulceraçion in lo so principio. E çoa ale piage de la neruci e de le
ecichue e ale ulceraçion in lo collo de la maire. questa fiore entra in le mexi
ne che se fa i pesani çoe che astenga liquore a la maire çoa al fluxo del sangue
de la maire e fasene empiastro de quello cum sugo de orço e cum el ulio
al corso de lo humore che uen a loro e a la infiaçon del stomego. E quando
questo fiore sebuta in una tela soura le bronce çoa al coloxe de loro. E cu
is le apostemaçion picole che uen in le raire de luna mescandole cum la i
miele. La uertu del unio. de questa uigna saluega e cum negro stipaco e çoa al
stomego. al quale coxe humore e a ibuega. E uniuersalmentir çoa a tutte
le infirmite in le quale e necessite de adunare e de stupicare.

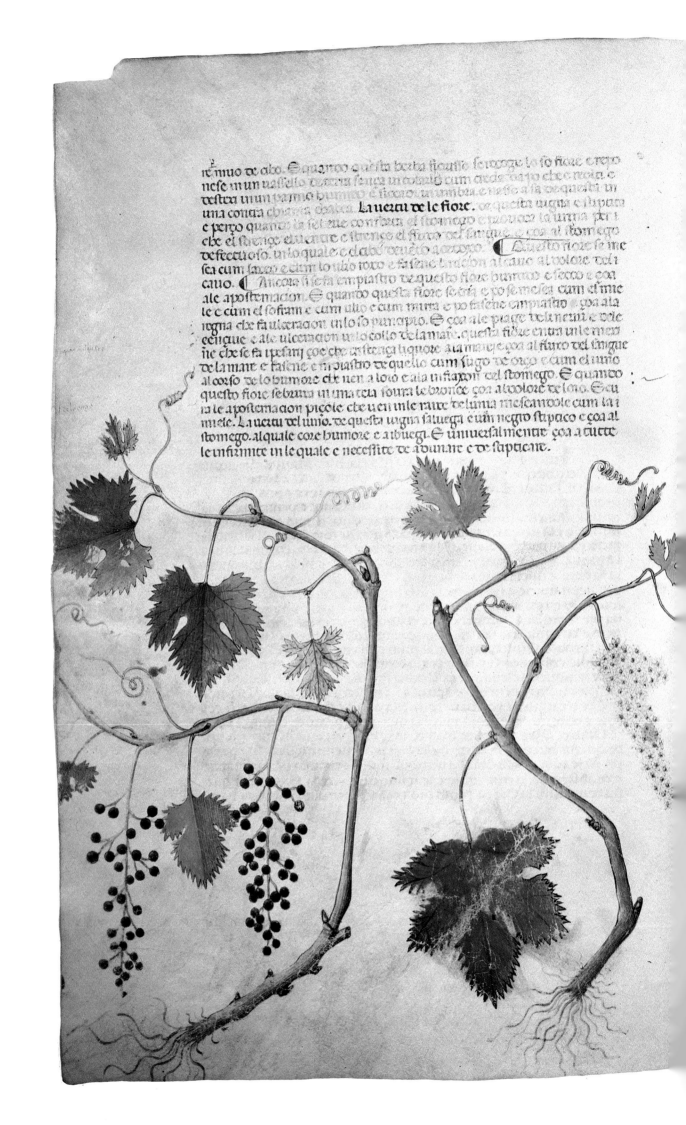

De la uigna desmestega. Capitolo.

La uigna desmestega che non se laoura dixe galieno che la uertu e
simele a la uigna saluega uien de soura noma dicte un pucho puis
nobele in uertu. Ancora dixe galieno che se foie de questo e luci
anoli quanto li se oua e fasene emplastro de questi son o cum el sugo i
pe loro mitiga le apostemation calde che e in lo stomego. El sugo de
le foie de questa uigna ena aquili che ba ulceration in li buodi e coa
la quili che spua sanguue ea quili che lame tange del bruxore del stomego.
e con ale gnauixe che ba la piera ciroco. e cosi sul cauro la de questa qua
uo el se sta infusion in laqua de queste e po benerie. E la lagrema de la ui
gna e simele ala gomma che se coaga sa soura li pampani la uertu de la gô
ma. E questa che leuando questa cum el uino ea sa fora la pus e fai
ne unction a la uiolega e sita cum e cosi aia regna ulcerola e no ulcerola
e couense ananti che se faga unction a questa uiolega lauare el mem
bro cum el sal mitro ecum lo alio spesse fieie pauore la pus. La lagre
ma che uen fura de le uenexe de la uigna quando la e fresca menar re
colte de la uigna e po metu in lo fugo cum un cauo chiuxa da laltro cauo
uen fura questa lagrema a muro sudore ba uertu desmouare le ueruxe
che uen chiama mirmice. La uertu de la cendexe de questa uencexa e de la
cendexe de le graspe de la uua de questa quando sen fa emplastro cum

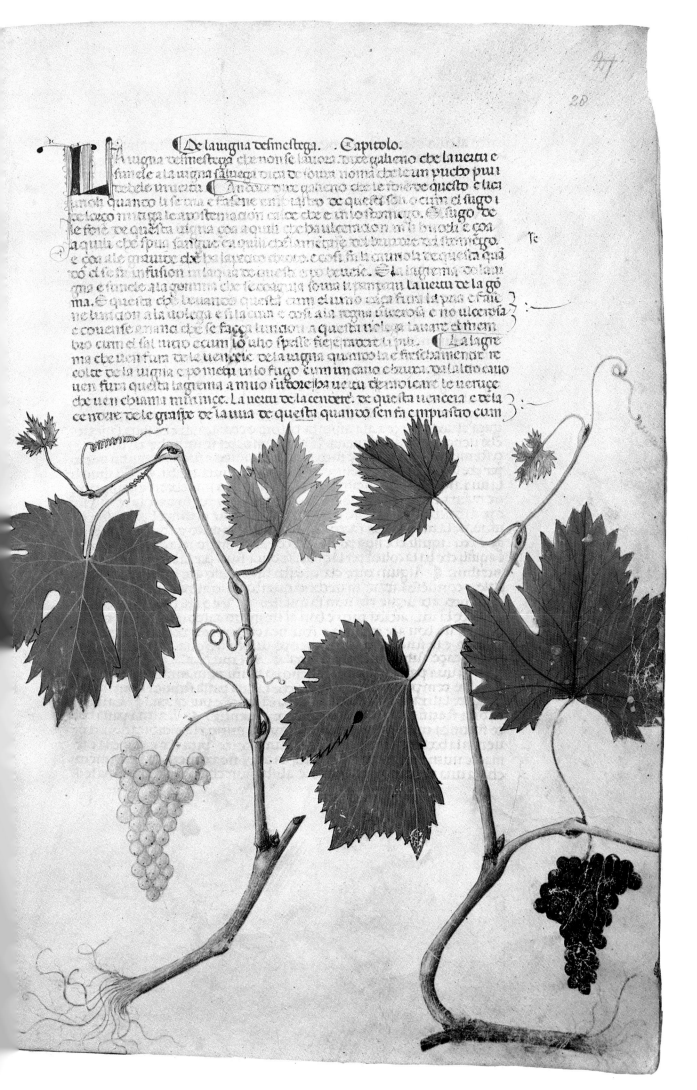

72

The Biblioteca Marciana in Venice is the proud possessor of a magnificent herbal containing nearly five hundred full-page paintings of plants by an otherwise unknown artist named Andrea Amadio. The text, an amalgam of information derived from many sources, is the work of an Italian physician, Benedetto Rinio, and according to Pächt the volume was compiled in the Veneto in 1419. Ettore de Toni, an Italian scholar who made a careful study of it about fifty years ago, proclaimed it 'indubitably from a pharmacognostic standpoint the most brilliant work of its century', and its illustrations – nearly ten times as many as those in Egerton 2020 – are as important as its text, even though it has now been established that some of them were copied.[1]

Ruskin, too, wrote enthusiastically of this 'wonderful MS.' which 'contained the earliest botanical drawings ... of approximate accuracy' that he knew, and he employed an artist, Antonio Caldara, to make copies of all the figures.[2] 'They are, however,' he adds, 'like all previous work, merely suggestive of the general character of the plant, and are very imaginative in details. ... Every plant, whatever its own complexity of growth, is reduced in this book to some balanced and ordered symmetry of arrangement; not, as in our base mechanical schools, by making one side of every leaf or cluster like its opposite, but by making them different, yet lovely in relation.'[3]

Ruskin was particularly struck by

a beautiful piece of fancy in the page representing the common blue chicory [*Cichorium intybus*]. Its current Latin name in the fifteenth century, from its rayed form, was 'Sponsa Solis'. But its blue colour caused it to be thought of as the favourite, not of the sun only, but of the sky, and the sun is drawn above it with a face, very beautiful, in the orb, surrounded by vermilion and golden rays, which descend to the flower, through undulating lines of blue, representing the air. I have never seen the united power of Apollo and Athena more prettily symbolised.

Amadio painted his plants in gouache on white paper and included their roots. Where trees and shrubs are portrayed there is inevitably some distortion of scale, but in general the naturalism of the treatment is remarkable. The colour is excellent, and the artist has not avoided the difficult task of representing a twisted leaf or a half-turned flower. If we except a few drawings which seem to be by another and inferior hand, the standard of work is uniformly high. The artist's skill as a colourist is well revealed in his treatment of the brilliant scarlet of the corn poppy and the glaucous green of the *Eryngium*, his delicacy of touch in the veinings upon the *Crocus sativus*, and his grasp of form and of rhythm in the drawing of millet.

On his death, Rinio left his herbal to his son Alberto with instructions that he should never part with this 'book of simples, painted from life [*sic*] and worth a small fortune'. But Alberto died in 1604 without issue and bequeathed it to the monks of SS. Giovanni e Paolo, who were instructed to guard it carefully, bind it with an iron chain to prevent theft, and allow it to be inspected only in the presence of two monks and by such men as were capable of benefiting by the study of it.

RINIO Liber de Simplicibus
The Veneto, 1419
28×20 cm ($11 \times 7\frac{7}{8}$ in)
483 folios
Biblioteca Nazionale Marciana,
Venice, Cod.Lat.VI 59
Colour plates p.74 Chicory
(*Cichorium intybus*); p.75 Corn poppy
(*Papaver rhoeas*).

1 Among the plants included, many – for example, the deadly nightshade (*Atropa belladonna*), *Hepatica triloba* and dyer's greenweed (*Genista tinctoria*) – are, so far as we know, here portrayed for the first time.
2 These copies, which were made between 1874 and 1877, are now in the library of Whitelands College, Putney. There is also a small volume of notes in Italian made by the artist about the illustrations.

3 Ruskin, *Works* Library edition, vol. XXI, 1906, pp. 142–43.

Rinio *Liber de Simplicibus, Cod. Lat. VI 59*, Pink (*Dianthus* sp.), painting by Amadio.

Opposite
Rinio *Liber de Simplicibus, Cod. Lat. VI 59*, Vine (*Vitis vinifera*), painting by Amadio, f90r.

363

pilago   ancipatus maior

Chaniparia maior

i caniperia m

Eupatoriu
Ancton
Gefit

folia pra
eupatorius

76

Opposite
Codex Bellunensis, Add. MS. 41623,
Edelweiss (*Leontopodium alpinum*),
f35v.

Left
Two endives (*Cichorium* sp.) on a leaf
of a north Italian herbal, formerly
owned by Wilfrid Blunt.

Codex Bellunensis
Belluno, fifteenth century
28.8 × 22.2 cm (11¾ × 8¾ in)
151 folios
British Library, London,
Add.MS.41623
Colour plates p.78 Winter cherry
(*Physalis alkekengi*), f70r; p.79
Martagon (*Lilium martagon*), f66v.

1 See *British Museum Quarterly* 3:
55–56 (1928).

The author and artist of this third Venetian herbal, the *Codex Bellunensis*,[1] whose text is largely drawn from Dioscorides, are not known, and its paintings, though vigorously executed in gouache and apparently made from life, are for the most part inferior to those in Egerton 2020.

Internal evidence establishes that it was compiled at Belluno, in the Venetian Alps about fifty miles to the north of Venice; it consequently contains paintings of a number of interesting alpines, including the first recorded figure of the edelweiss (*Leontopodium alpinum*). This dull member of the Compositae, whose renown far exceeds its beauty, was named by Dioscorides, but it is possible that he used 'Leontopodion' as a name for some other plant, for the edelweiss hardly suggests a lion's paw. In the Belluno herbal the flower is backed by a red shield.

An Italian flower album made about 1700, given to a Somerset clergyman in 1719 and now in a private collection in Wells, includes faithful copies of plants from the *Codex Bellunensis*.

The scattered leaves of another north Italian herbal – many of them in the Senckenberg Library in Frankfurt – resemble a less skilful version of Rinio's. One shows a mallow (*Malva* sp.) with its root system; another, two endives.

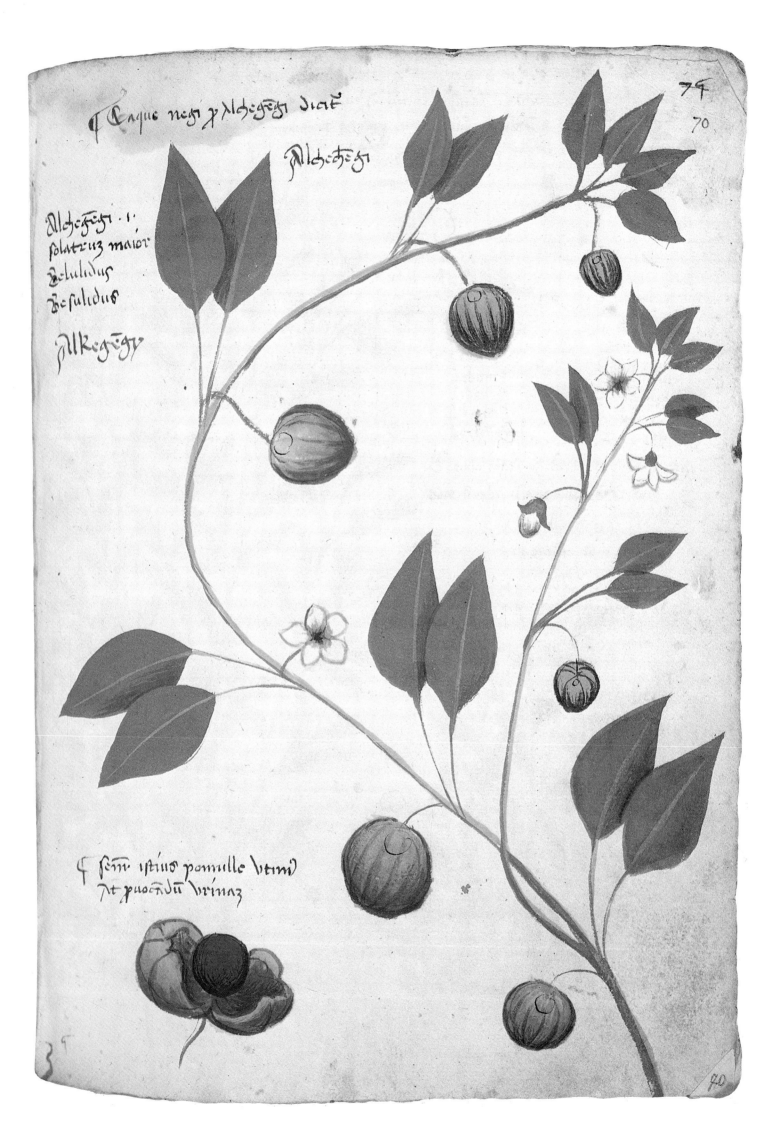

℩ Caquo negi y Aldchegegi dicat

Aldchegegi

Aldchegegi ·i·
folatruz maior
Zetulidus
Zetulidus

Alkegegy

℩ sem istius pomulle venni
At puocandu vrinaz

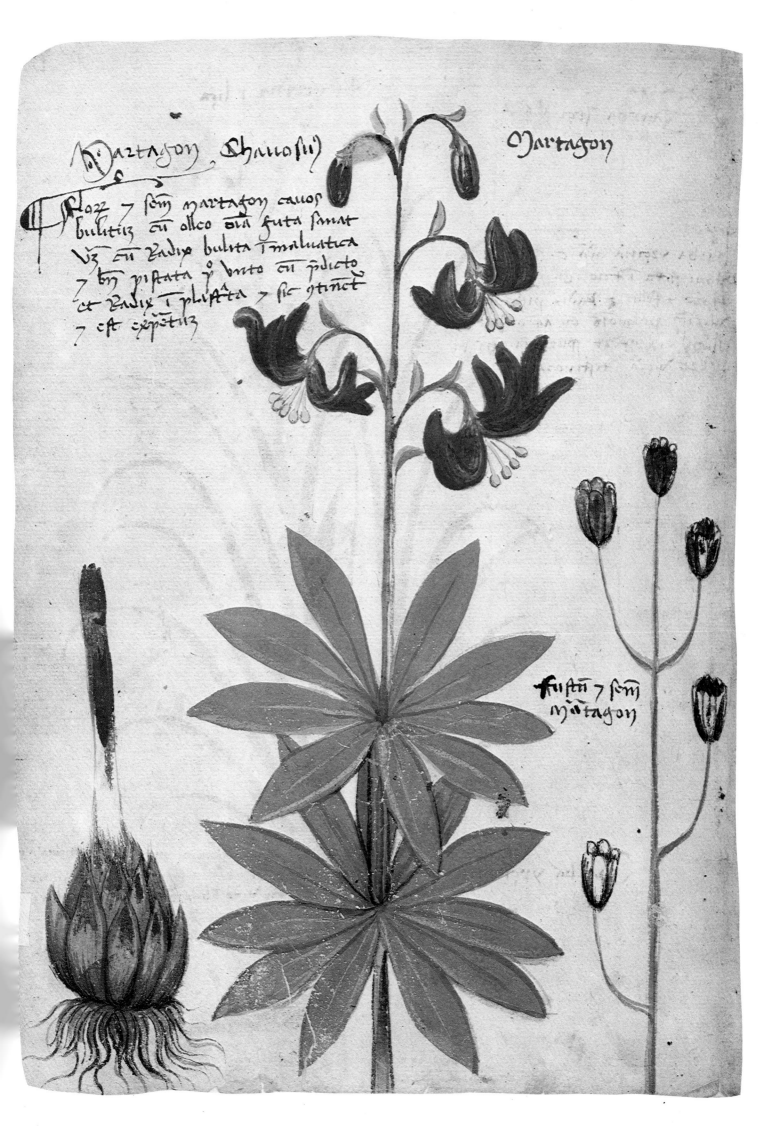

Martagon Chanossij   Martagon

Flor 7 sem martagon cauos
bulitiz cu olleo oia futa sanat
viz cu radicz bulita i maluatica
7 bn pistata in vnto cu pdicto
et radix i plistata 7 sic gtinet
7 est experimentu

fustu 7 sem
matagon

On lieu ou on la frote Elle
n verta ardant ¶ Contre
les vers qui sont es oreilles
le jus dicelle degoute dedans
vrtut les / vers qui y sont

fistule Et la escarfeit
conuenablement et
la orte et gravit Elle
croist en lieux plains
et sablonneux

Parauelle ou pa
relle cest une herbe
dont les foulles ressamblent
a foulles de laubee on naust
le propolre On est samblable
a une herbe que on appelle
listvaige Et a semenre longe
et ronde a maniere de ich
¶ Sa raine est longue
et grosse et a couleur iaune
Aulcuns lappellent lerbe bast
ligne pource quelle est
venimeuse Aulcuns dient
que ont fait delle bonne
advisement ¶ Elle
vault pruncipalment vote
fistule se on en fait une
fente laquelle on mect
dedans le tron de la

Punpernelle
est une herbe
qui naist en lieu sablon
neux au pied des mon
taignes Elle vault
pruncipalment pour seffon
der playes Et son la
poulce faute delle mist
sus soulant et elle est
sessondre ¶ Contre fi
stule et chancre se on la
mist dessus on verde on
seche elle y proffite
¶ Pour lobstruite des
yeux souent lauee de
leaue ou du vin on elle
auva este vnte au sow
et au matins ¶ Cote
venuum et contre la moe
sue des serpens le jus
delle donne a boyre

No less interesting than these northern manuscripts is the mid-fifteenth-century Italian *Erbario Medicinale*[1] which contains 204 paintings of medicinal plants with notes on their virtues. The text appears to be original, though clearly derived from standard medieval works on the subject. The page illustrated here shows a species of *Aristolochia*, or birthwort. The plant is so called, says Dioscorides, 'because it is thought to help passing well women in child-bed'. (*Aristos* is the Greek for 'best', *locheia* for 'parturition'.) It was, however, also recommended by various herbalists in cases of snake-bite, and for the treatment of innumerable other complaints ranging from hiccups to asthma.

A French manuscript of the *Livre des Simples Médicines* (*c.* 1450), much more medieval in character, is even more attractive. It was written at Cluny for a member of the Dubois family, and its text, a translation of the already-mentioned *Liber de Simplici Medicina* of Platearius, closely resembles that of the first printed edition of *Le Grant Herbier*. Its four hundred and more little paintings of plants, arranged alphabetically, are inserted in text written in double columns. The plate here reproduced gives a good idea of their quality and charm.

In the Bibliothèque Royale Albert I in Brussels there is another manuscript (IV 1024) of the *Livre des Simples Médicines*, which presumably dates from the close of the fifteenth century. Of its 455 illustrations, 398 are of plants. Dr Carmélia Opsomer, who has edited a fine facsimile edition of the manuscript,[2] alleges that the best of the plant paintings are drawn from nature – a feature she believes to be unique in fifteenth-century herbals with the exception of those in Rinio, which they are said to resemble. As has already been pointed out, many of the paintings in Rinio are themselves copied from an earlier manuscript.

Erbario Medicinale (Medicinal Herbal)
Italy, mid-fifteenth century
38 × 24 cm (15 × 9½ in)
106 folios
Wellcome Institute for the History of Medicine, London, MS.336
Colour plate p.82 Birthwort (*Aristolochia clematitis*), f8v.

1 See P. Johnston-Saint (1938).

PLATEARIUS
Livre des Simples Médicines
Cluny, *c.* 1480
28 × 19 cm (11 × 7½ in)
316 folios
Wellcome Institute for the History of Medicine, London. MS.626
Colour plate p.83 Mouse-ear hawkweed (*Hieracium pilosella*) and periwinkle (*Vinca* sp.), f209r.

2 Published in 1981–82 by De Schutter S.A. of Antwerp in two volumes, with text in French, English and German.

Opposite
Platearius *Livre des Simples Médicines*, Wellcome, *MS. 626*, Sorrel (*Rumex acetosa*) and burnet (*Sanguisorba officinalis*), f208v.

Aristologia longa e di simile natura e co la rotonda excepto che la longa e
de piu debile opatione e spesso e piu uirtuose a fare nascere la carne de
le piaghe che sono nela matrice e nele altre piaghe

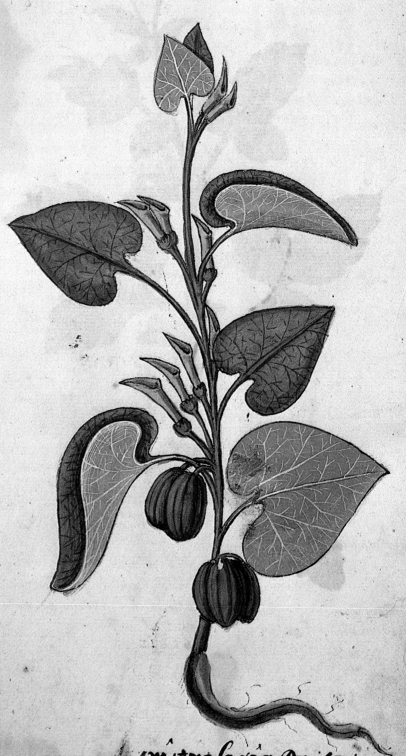

aristologia Ro Lon:

Aristologia longa e di simile natura e co la rotonda excepto che la longa e
de piu debile opatione e spesso e piu uirtuose a fare nascere la carne de
le piaghe che sono nela matrice e nele altre piaghe

bonne hors tout venin po²
ſauoir ſe aulcun nauwe de
playe vinua on mowa
ſoit vne poignie de pimpre-
nelle pillee auec du ſel
et en ſoit le ſus eſpraint
Et puis ſoit deſtrampe
en vng petit voire de vin
et ſoit donne a boire au
malade Et ſe on voit le
bruuaige iſſir par la
playe je neſchappera
point et hy donne a ſonger

.343.

Et de reſſondre playes.
¶ Pour playes reſondre
et reſſondre ſoit fait oingne-
ment de ſon ſus auec cire
et oile et ſe rebouture
On que ſon ſus ſus les
playes. on reſpande en
ſeim ¶ Et la pouldre
ſeiche de ſes fenlles je
reſſonde tantoſt les playes
nouuelles ¶ Contre
fiebre quarte ſoit le ſus
de pillireſte donne a boire
en temps que laccres dure
et le malade ſera gary
¶ Pour ſauoir ſe aul-
cuy malade mourra on
vinua ſoit donne le ſus.
jcelle aboire Et ſe la
maladie le ſuroſe je
mourra ſenon je garra
¶ Item ſe on trampe
vng tranchant dancun
coutel ou eſpee dedans
le ſus. le tranchant ton
pora et tranchera tout
aultres tranchans.

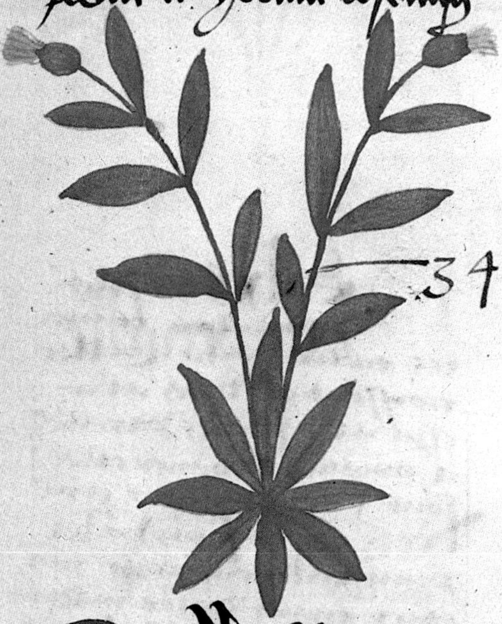

Pilloſelle ou
pillireſte ceſt
vne herbe qui croit aupre
des montaignes Et a
feulles mains longues de
vng doy et a poil en ſes
feulles aſſes longue Et
poutre lappelle pillireſte
ou pilloſelle et ſe eſtent
et eſpart ſus terre ¶ Elle
a vertu de eſtraindre
mondiſier ſuſtoyer.

.34

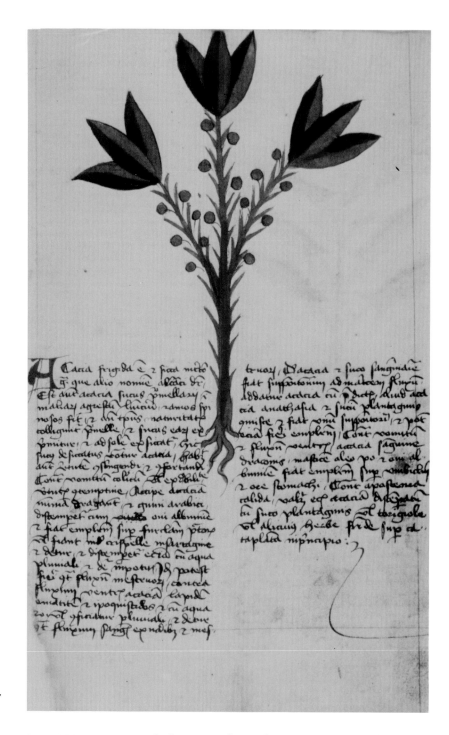

Tractatus de Herbis, Cod. MSS. 604,
'Acacia' (*Acacia senegal*).

Tractatus de Herbis
North of the Alps(?), mid-fifteenth
century
28.5 × 21–21.5 cm ($11\frac{1}{4}$ × $8\frac{1}{4}$ − $8\frac{1}{2}$ in)
180 folios
Universitätsbibliothek, Munich,
Cod.MSS.604

In 1926, F. Hommel discovered in the University Library in
Munich a previously unrecognized and badly damaged mid-
fifteenth-century *Tractatus de Herbis* or 'Lexicon Plantarum', at
first considered to stem from the Veneto. It contains more than
four hundred figures of plants, carried out in pen-and-wash,
together with simple remedies associated with them and other
miscellaneous matter, and was apparently written for the use of a
hospital. The 'Acacia' we reproduce is believed to be *Acacia
senegal*, the source of gum arabic which had been imported into
Europe from the Middle East for some two thousand years.

Stylistically the work shows some resemblance to the Vienna
Tacuinum Sanitatis, understood to have been in Innsbruck at that
time, and there now seems to be a possibility that the *Tractatus*
was actually compiled somewhere north of the Alps rather than
in Italy. It was skilfully and extensively restored in 1974.

The library of the University of Vermont possesses an Italian herbal of approximately the same date as the preceding one. Its illustrations are as entertaining as they are perplexing. Of the two we reproduce, one presumably shows Adam, Eve, and some serpents, together with several plants, one of which may be a species of *Stachys*. The other is topped by a polypody, while below is a curious scene, captioned 'Arghomento', of a rabbit hunt with two nude figures. *Argomento*, according to Italian dictionaries, means 'argument, reason, proof; sign; subject'; but the text accompanying each refers only to the virtues of the plants and offers no explanation of the presence of the figures of animals. The polypody is described as having no flowers or seeds, its roots being black externally and yellow within. There follows a receipt for its use as a febrifuge.

The manuscript belonged at one time to Lucius E. Chittenden, a New York attorney who was Register of the Treasury under President Lincoln.

Herbal in Italian
Italy, *c.* 1500
33 × 23 cm (13 × 9 in)
141 folios
University of Vermont Library,
Burlington, 580.9 M31–45.716
Colour plates p.86 Adam, Eve and
serpents with 'Erba consolida
maggiore' and 'Erba brettonicha'
(*Stachys* sp.), f34r; p.87 'Polipodio'
(*Polypodium vulgare*) and a rabbit
hunt, f69r.

Erba consolida mag comelella et morbida ico
elfiore cenuno labarba nera difuory et giore fa lanfo bugla pimida
nafce iluoghy domeftichy et morti ze di lore dibomina quaſi
et ciaſcuna vale achi e crepato ch riſtrigne branca dentro mucellaginoſa z na ivmiore
impraſtro ſalda in quaranta di et riſtrigne rugiory cioe maggiore meri et ſime
menſtruo ze molto ſtrectuia adogni choſa Raſſerma loſſa rotte T. 25 dy beuta cū vino
Elſole colmele vale ytro caligine dochy . Et beuto elſugho con vino vale amorſo diſerpe.

Erba brettonicha e calda iſeccha in tergo grado vale adolory z dutij di corpo zdimatrice vſadola
verde in lattouaro ochome laducha dimangiarla O vſandola i poluere vale ytro amorſo diſer
poute dato ilſuo ſugo bere olerba man giare vale amatory che naſ mo nella bocha dentro
e alle gengie corrofe et ulcerate te nendo ilſugo i bocha ole fogle maſticate leſalda
zguariſce riſtrigne elſangue ſalda leferite zulcere . mitigha elmale caducho aman
giarla zvſarla . Vale aunfirmita dochy ilſugo ſuo cō acqua roſata . Et expme loſſa fra
chate zrotte dalaltre ſpachate Purgha lefiſtole zleferite ztaglature
zmorby corigugne iſalda lepariti ta glate. Alemembra paralitiche poſta ſu peſti
da zriſta ſalute vale alla ſcancha cotta i vino zſudo ipiaſtro
achi vrina ſangue data a mangiare freſcha o ipoluere
p quindici di ſana .

erba difaturno.

.C. Sii. g.

Polipodio querino eherba ... laquale nasce i sileri di a zapie
querre i pero e dedto poli podio querino i nelle medii ne ... delle
radice uno lerba i nasce an chora nelle saxa i falle mu ... fi pone la
a fecrho mali ... ricar ſcope
quello ch ſi ... megliore i piu optimo i ſi truoua a pie delle querre

Et fa la fogla quaſi ſimile alla giſfelce i uo fa neſiore neſeme la radice ſui et neru diſicory i gialla
dentro Et detta barba colta neta i ſecha ſipuo ſbaue due anni cū molta efficacia et e calda
interzo grado i ſecha i ſeio grado ſo auicenna lib. 2°. Et ha uirtu da trarre i daſoluere et
purgha lomore flematicho i malichonicho i pero e ynemente nelle mediane ouero decochion
flegnatiche i malichonicho Nota ẽ nelle decochion debbia porre cō eſſo coſe ch iſilueny
lauentoſita ſichome Carui. Aniſi. Maratry chomino eſimili. vale gra diata paſſione la
ſua decochione. Rō polipodio .z.j. prune .uij. Aniſi. ſquinah uiole an p. z. j. et fa de
cocchione dalla lamatina mezo bichiery. Et vale ancho alla cotidiana febbre. iſ. Rō
uno pollo graſſo vechio i uendelo et chuocilo i uotalo delle budella Et necto lome pi
dipolipodio .z. uij. finochio .z. ſ. cenmamomo gharofany cardamomo an .z.j. ſ.
non moſtade. 8 pugho an .z.j. peſta ogny coſa i i metti nel detto pollo i fa chuocerr
tanto chelpollo ſia diſfacto i cola i colatura diſsoluy z. j di bene decto i fa criſtero a
male diſfacho i ytra ogny ventoſita Et a male di matrice data la decochione bere
aladonna ſenza labenedecta uno bichiery caldo i a tucte le paſſiony di ventoſita octo i
acqua o vino cioe polipodio finochio .z. d. ij. dermodachly peſti. j

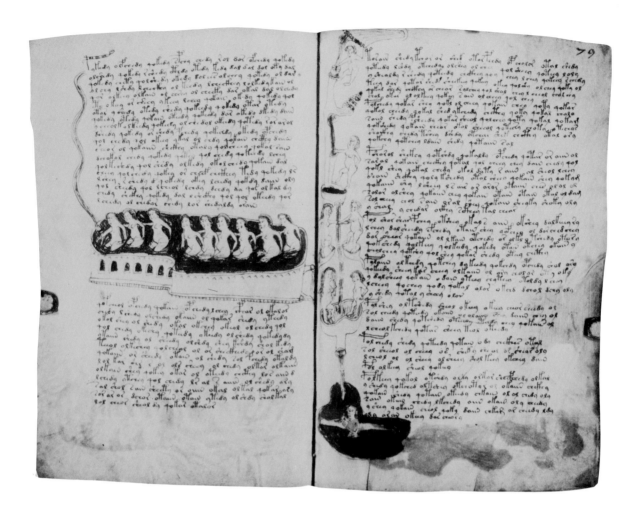

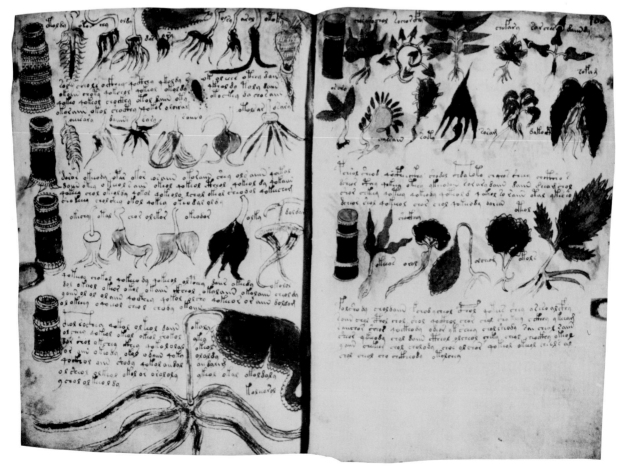

'The most mysterious manuscript in the world' was Professor John M. Manley's description of the so-called 'Roger Bacon Cipher Manuscript', presented in 1969 to the Yale University Library.

The text is in a cipher which has baffled every cryptographic expert from Athanasius Kircher (1602–80) down to the present day, though quite recently some of the plant and star names have been decoded.[1] Some four hundred of its fantastic illustrations are of botanical subjects, and one page shows apothecary jars together with the plants they are intended to contain. But 'while everything – including what appears to be a pharmacist's mortar and pestle – makes the book look like a herbal', Alfred Werner considers that this might be 'little more than crafty camouflage' to mislead 'the authorities'[2] – whoever they may have been. The remainder of the figures are principally of astrological or 'biological' intent, a number of the latter including obese little nude females apparently taking baths, while there is one that is described by Werner as 'a plumber's dream' – though 'Heath Robinson nightmare' might seem more appropriate.

A previous owner of the manuscript, the New York bookseller H. P. Kraus, who presented it to Yale, wrote of it:

> The illusion of realistic portrayal is dispelled after the first few pages by the occurrence of obviously fantastic elements in the flower and root structures of some of the plants. Increasingly we realise that we have before us in this manuscript the work of a highly ingenious artist of most extraordinary visionary powers. . . . The diagrammatic drawings of small-scale female nudes, immersed and emerging from fluids or interconnecting tubes and capsules, give the impression that the artist was struggling with the very mystery of the creation of life itself.

A Blake before his time?

There is no question of the manuscript being a modern fake, its purchase by Rudolf II, Holy Roman Emperor (1576–1612), being established beyond all reasonable doubt and its pedigree from 1666 onward being impeccable. Rudolf believed it to be the work of the famous 'Roger Bacon, the Englishman', who lived in the thirteenth century; but our manuscript was almost certainly written – though nobody knows where – at a later date, probably in the fifteenth or sixteenth century. The Emperor may possibly have acquired it from the library of John Dee, the sixteenth-century English astrologer and mathematician, known to be a collector of Roger Bacon manuscripts, who was in Prague from 1582 to 1586.

It seems almost incredible that, so far, even computers have failed to decipher any of the main text, though a number of false claims have been made over the years. The recent labours of Brumbaugh would, however, seem to suggest that the mystery may soon be solved. We need another Ventris.

Voynich 'Roger Bacon' Cipher Manuscript
Fifteenth or sixteenth century
22.9 × 15.2 cm (9 × 6 in)
116 folios
plus 'several large folding sheets'
Yale University Library, New Haven, MS.408
Colour plates pp.90–91 'Sunflowers', ff33v–34r.

1 See R. S. Brumbaugh (1974), pp. 546–48 for the plant names, and *Journal of the Warburg and Courtauld Institutes XXXIX* (1976), pp. 139–50 for the star names. For the almost endless literature dealing with this manuscript see *The Yale University Library Gazette*, April 1978, p. 272.
2 Alfred Werner (1963), pp. 4–9.

Opposite
Voynich 'Roger Bacon' Cipher Manuscript, MS. 408.

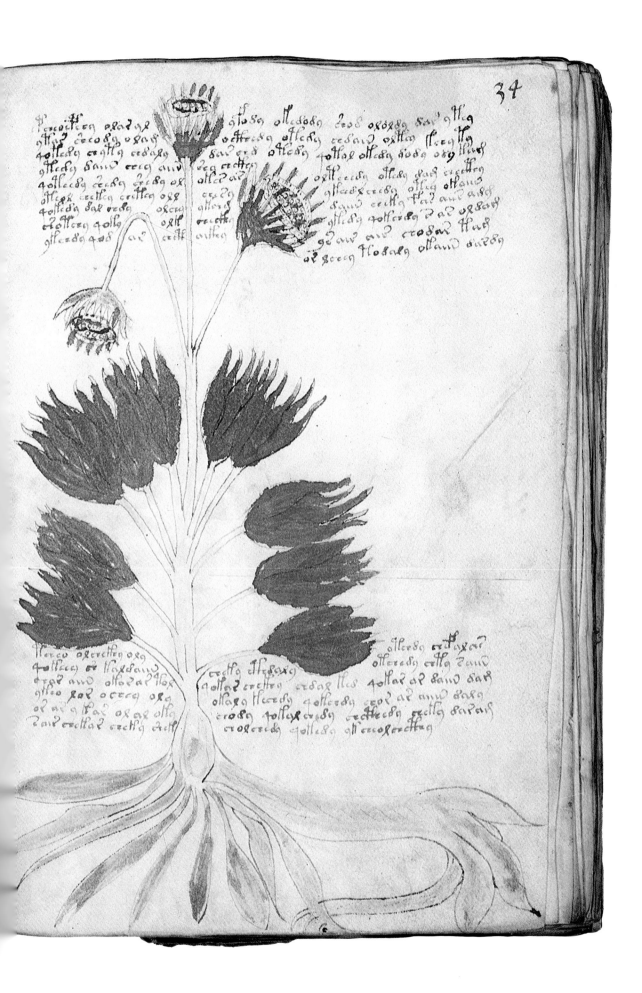

Auslasser *Herbal in German, Clm.
5905*, Grass of Parnassus (*Parnassia
palustris*), f135r.

AUSLASSER Herbal in German
Ebersberg (?), 1479
22 × 16 cm (8¾ × 6¼ in)
200 folios of 305 in the volume
*Bayerische Staatsbibliothek, Munich,
Clm.5905*

The introduction to this German herbal explains that 'it was illustrated by Brother Vitus Auslasser of Fümpp near Swaz' (Schwaz, in the Tyrol) who was a monk and teacher at the monastery of St. Sebastian in Ebersberg. Its 198 figures of plants are crude, but decorative and in the main easily identifiable; some seem to be related to one of the earliest printed herbals, the *German Herbarius*, published in Mainz in 1485 (see p. 115).

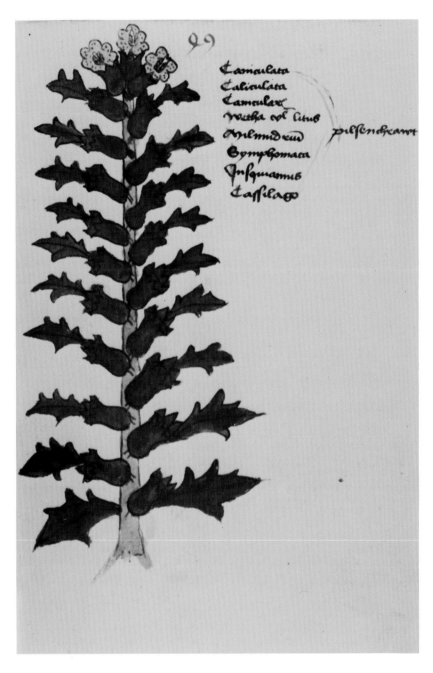

Auslasser *Herbal in German, Clm. 5905*, Henbane (*Hyoscyamus* sp.), f143r.

A most engaging herbal, compiled in north Italy about 1500, probably also comes from the hand of a German artist. One page shows the carline thistle, so named after Charlemagne. The Emperor, stricken by the plague when on a campaign, is said to have prayed to God, who in answer despatched an angel to indicate by shooting with an arrow the plant needed to cure him. The carline thistle, *Carlina acaulis*, is (as *acaulis* implies) sessile in Britain, but it is not infrequently found on the Continent with a substantial stem. A German name for the plant, 'Englische Distel', is of course the 'angelic' (*not* 'English') thistle.

Another figure in this delightful book portrays the mandrake with horn-blowing herbalist and hound. Embedded in the earth from the knees down, the mandrake displays root-like fingers. On its head it bears a fruit of the plant and two impaled, severed hands; the latter are a reminder that an infusion of the root of mandragora in wine was used as an anaesthetic during amputations. The Germans call the plant *Alraun*, as inscribed below the Latin name on the drawing.

Pflanzenbuch (Book of Plants)
Northern Italy, *c.* 1500
31 × 22 cm (12¼ × 8¾ in)
62 folios of 81 in the volume
Bayerische Staatsbibliothek, Munich, Cod.icon.(bot.) 26
Colour plates p.94 Charlemagne and carline thistle (*Carlina acaulis*), f8v; p.95 Mandrake (*Mandragora autumnalis*), f59r.

Carlina

Mandragora
Alraun

Although by the close of the fifteenth century a number of printed herbals had already been published, it will be more convenient to deal first with some of the principal manuscript herbals of the sixteenth century. However, when considering the latter it is important to note that we shall deliberately defer a discussion of three important collections of botanical drawings of this period since they are directly associated with printed herbals, the subject of the second part of this book. These are the lovely paintings made by Hans Weiditz for Brunfels's *Herbarum Vivae Eicones* (1530–36), the more pedestrian work of Albrecht Meyer and his partners for Leonhart Fuchs's *De Historia Stirpium* (1542), and the great corpus of botanical studies by Pierre van der Borcht and others assembled by Clusius for various publications of the famous Plantin press in Antwerp.

We now reach that difficult moment when the herbal is merging, at times almost imperceptibly, into the florilegium. We also have floras of a particular country, in which the virtues of the plants are often included. Many botanical manuscripts contain paintings both of humble plants clearly admitted for their culinary or medicinal use, and of garden plants given a place for their beauty alone. By the seventeenth century the distinction between herbal and florilegium is usually, but by no means always, more clear: for example, nobody could possibly claim that the two splendid volumes of flower paintings, made about 1650 by Johann Walther for Johann Count of Nassau[1] to illustrate the treasures of his garden at Schloss Idstein near Frankfurt am Main, were anything but florilegia. What, therefore, we choose to include or exclude must on occasions be rather arbitrary, and the temptation to stray a little from the strait and narrow path of the herbal proper has sometimes proved irresistible.

1 Now in the Victoria and Albert Museum, London.

PLATEARIUS Livre des Simples Médicines
Paris, early sixteenth century
34 × 25.8 cm (13⅜ × 10⅛ in)
197 folios
Bibliothèque Nationale, Paris, MS.12322
Colour plate p.98 Solomon's seal (*Polygonatum odoratum*), *Rosa gallica* and a male *Saturnia pyri* moth, f143v.

One of the latest extant manuscripts of the *Livres des Simples Médicines* was made in Paris by the Capucins of the rue Saint-Honoré. From the close similarity of its illustrations to those of the famous *Book of Hours* illuminated by Jean Bourdichon between 1500 and 1508 for Anne of Brittany, it can be attributed to the opening years of the sixteenth century. The latter included about 337 plants in its borders. They are often painted, as in a herbal, complete with bulbs or roots; insects, snails and other small animals crawl over the flowers and leaves.

The paintings in this *Livre des Simples Médicines* are collected together at the end of the manuscript. Folio 143v shows a gallica rose on which a moth, a male *Saturnia pyri*, a larger relative of the Emperor moth, has alighted, and Solomon's seal (*Polygonatum odoratum*). These plants are often found together in religious paintings – for example, in the Van Eyck altarpiece at Ghent – since both were associated with the Virgin Mary. Another name for Solomon's seal was *Sigillum benedictae virginis*: seal of the Blessed Virgin. Herbalists thought very highly of the efficacy of this plant. Strewn on the floor of a room it banished 'serpents and all venemous creatures' from the house, and according to Gerard its root, when applied freshly gathered, 'taketh away in one night, or two at the most, any bruse, blacke or blew spots gotten by fals, or womens wilfulnes, in stumbling upon their hastie husbands fists, or such like'.

Herbal and Bestiary ('Mellon' copy)
Cowslip (*Primula veris*), columbine
(*Aquilegia* sp.), corn-cockle
(*Agrostemma githago*) and bladder
campion (*Silene* sp.).

Herbal and Bestiary
England, *c.* 1520
41.5 × 28 cm (16¾ × 11 in)
50 folios
Bodleian Library, Oxford,
MS.Ashmole 1504
Colour plate p.99 Foxglove (*Digitalis*
purpurea) and fennel (*Foeniculum*
vulgare), f15v.

Though clearly made for an East Anglian client, a manuscript dating from about 1520 and once owned by Elias Ashmole may have been the work of an artist from across the North Sea. The plants depicted, followed by drawings of animals, letters and items of household equipment, are grouped two to a page in an alphabetical series of their English names. This attractive book, though usually described as a herbal and bestiary, might also have been either a pattern-book for craftsmen decorating their work or an entertaining book for teaching children.

A not quite identical twin of this manuscript, with four plants to a page and less non-botanical material, was once in the library at Helmingham Hall in Suffolk. This version was bought by Paul Mellon at Sotheby's in June 1961 and is now in his collection in Virginia. Both manuscripts were reproduced in facsimile in a single volume in 1988.

Anthera

Sigillum sctē m

Fox gloues. Fenel.

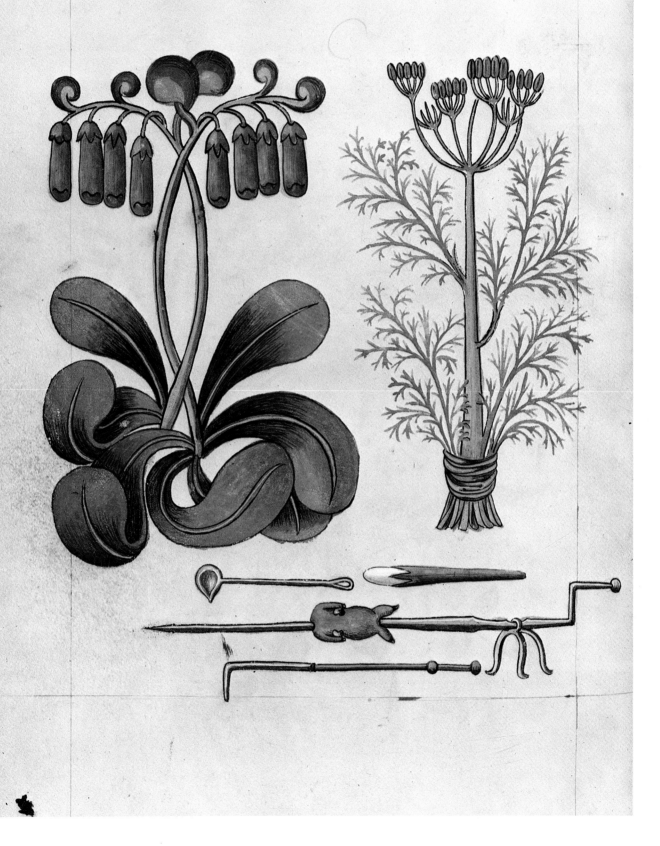

Pier Antonio Michiel (1510–66), the compiler of this fine herbal, was a Venetian patrician who was at one time director of the Botanical Gardens at Padua.

Of the artist, Domenico dalle Greche, who produced a large part of the one thousand or so paintings that illustrate its five volumes, nothing further appears to be known. The best of them – for example those of *Orchis purpurea* and 'Spatola phetida' (*Iris foetidissima*) – are admirable, and presumably some of the less successful are by another and an inferior hand. His *Tulipa sylvestris* and *T. praecox* must be among the earliest representations of the genus. There are also some crude but engaging pages enlivened by the introduction of birds, insects, and naive little landscapes.

It is interesting to compare Domenico dalle Greche's painting of a carline thistle with that of another of some fifty years earlier, reproduced on page 94. The latter is thoroughly Teutonic and undoubtedly decorative; but the artist has either totally misunderstood the leaves and flower-head of the carline thistle or worked from a different member of the thistle family. Its treatment recalls that of the gay murals still to be found on the façades of the houses in many Bavarian and Tyrolean villages. Domenico's painting is admirable in every way, and shows the great competence of the best Italian botanical artists of the period.

Michiel returned to Venice in 1555, where he cultivated a garden containing many exotics from the Levant and elsewhere, among them the white form of the oleander (*Nerium oleander*) which he was the first to grow in Italy.

MICHIEL Cinque Libri di Piante
(Five Books of Plants)
30×21 cm ($11\frac{3}{4} \times 8\frac{1}{4}$ in)
128 folios
Venice, mid-sixteenth century
Biblioteca Nazionale Marciana,
Venice,
Cod. Marc. It. II 29
Colour plates p.102 Thistle (*Carlina acaulis* subsp. *simplex*), f105r; p.103 Lady orchid (*Orchis purpurea*), f49r.

Opposite
Michiel *Cinque Libri di Piante, Cod. Marc. It. II 29*, Fumitory (*Fumaria officinalis*), f76r.

101

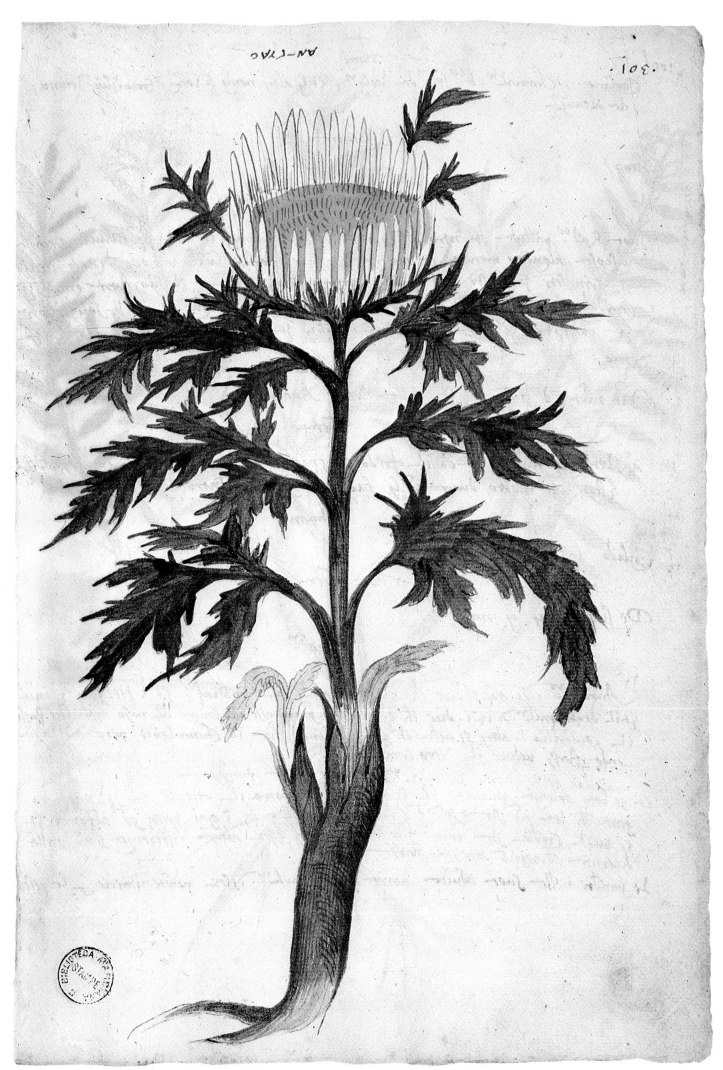

103

'Aquileia' (*Aquilegia* sp.), Hunt Institute Collection, Pittsburgh.

LIGOZZI Watercolours

Verona, late sixteenth century
Galleria degli Uffizi, Florence
Colour plates p.106 Valerian (*Valeriana rubra*): the insect is *Clerus apiarus*; p.107 Fig (*Ficus carica*): the birds shown are *Vidua erythrorhyncha, Steganura paradisea* and *Hypochera chalybeata*.

In Verona we find a further north Italian botanical and zoological artist of outstanding ability at work in the latter part of the sixteenth century: Jacopo Ligozzi (1547–1626). Though his flower paintings cannot strictly be considered to constitute a herbal, many of the plants he chose were of medicinal importance – for example our common foxglove (*Digitalis purpurea*) of which he made a study so in advance of his time that it might well have served William Curtis for his *Flora Londinensis* of two centuries later. No less striking are those of a fig with three birds, and another of valerian with a small insect.

Ligozzi, a versatile artist who also worked in oils and in tempera, became court painter in Florence to the Grand Duke of Tuscany and other Medici princes, and was appointed Superintendent of the Uffizi Gallery, where many of his finest paintings are still preserved; others are in the University Library at Bologna. Ulisse Aldrovandi, previously mentioned as one-time owner of Egerton 2020, was a personal friend of Ligozzi, of whose ceaseless industry and high talent he wrote: 'A most excellent artist who has no other care day or night but to paint plants and animals of every kind.' A major exhibition of his natural history paintings was staged at the Uffizi in 1924. They have been shown often since then, especially the flowers.

Erbario Miniato, Windsor, Foxglove, (*Digitalis purpurea*), f201r.

The Hunt Institute for Botanical Documentation at Pittsburgh describes its interesting collection of sixty-six oil and water-colour botanical paintings, carried out in north Italy *c.* 1595, as a florilegium; but it might with equal accuracy be termed a herbal, since many of the plants illustrated are of medical interest. The figure shows the unknown artist's painting of 'Aquileia' (*Aquilegia* sp.), whose leaves and seeds were sometimes used in a lotion to relieve a sore throat and pains in the liver respectively.

A large part of another Italian manuscript, called the *Erbario Miniato*, is now in the Royal Library at Windsor, and a few other leaves from it were sold by Sotheby's, New York, on 16–17 September 1988. The herbal was once in the collection of Cassiano dal Pozzo (1588–1657), naturalist, antiquarian, and an early member of the Accademia dei Lincei. He commissioned many drawings for his 'museum on paper', including some of the plants in this herbal, which he added to earlier acquisitions. References in the plant labels to Mattioli and other botanical books underline the scholarly intention of the herbal.

Erbario Miniato (Painted Herbal)
Italy, early seventeenth century
42 × 27 cm (16½ × 10⅝ in)
211 folios
Royal Library, Windsor
RL 27691-27901

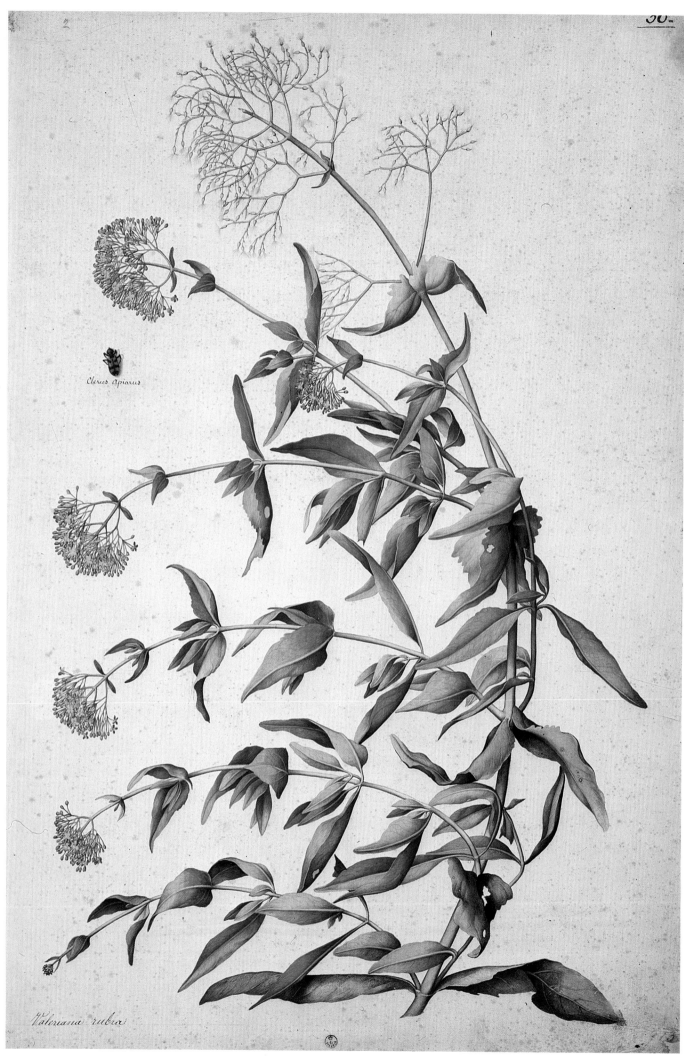

Clerus Apiarius

Valeriana rubra

Ficus Carica, Emberiza Paradisea.

Tlahculol Tomazqtl. Tlancxtiquauitl. Xococqua. Tepapaquilti qua
quaq̃ uitl.   uit. tl.   uitl.

Temahuiz quanhhuitzih Eloxochitl. Yzquixo quetzalylin
tliquauitl. Bilxochitl.   chitl.

108

Finally we turn from Europe to the New World. The so-called 'Badianus Herbal' was compiled in 1552 by two Aztecs at the Roman Catholic College of Santa Cruz, and was dedicated to Don Francisco, son of the first Viceroy to New Spain; it was rediscovered in the Vatican Library in 1931. Its great interest lies in the fact that, so far as is known, it is the earliest of such works to have been produced in America, and its figures, though suggesting comparison with those in the *Herbal of Apuleius Platonicus* and the *Hortus Sanitatis*, are thought not to have been influenced by European models. The joint authors were Martin de la Cruz – 'an Indian physician ... who is not theoretically learned, but taught only by experience', and Juannes Badianus who provided the Latin translation. A facsimile edition was published in America in 1940.[1]

No prettier herbal could well be imagined, though almost all of the 180 medicinal plants portrayed would have posed a serious problem to the would-be gatherer. This is a pity, since the identification of the herb guaranteed to be 'useful in curing the fatigue of men working in government departments' would be of value today. The names of the two lefthand plants illustrated on p.110 are translated as 'deer liver' and 'blue medicine'; the third is our still-popular marvel of Peru. The author comments: 'When instilled into discharging ears the root of Maçayelli, the seed of Xoxouhquipahtli and some leaves of Tlaquilin with a pinch of salt in hot water are very helpful.' The pinch of salt is clearly an important ingredient.

A copy of the Badianus herbal, commissioned by Cassiano dal Pozzo for his own museum, was made in Rome in 1626–7 and is now in the Royal Library at Windsor.

Only five of the seven plants on the page reproduced here have been included in our illustration. The first two of these are both for the treatment of sore or swollen eyes, the remaining three are narcotics. Azcapanyxhua Tlahçolpahtli is translated as 'medicine from an ant-hill', and the ants are shown crawling on its roots. The second may be a mimosa; the remainder cannot be identified. A paragraph about sleep-inducing plants is followed by one on how to keep awake by throwing some of your own hair on burning embers and sniffing the resultant fumes.

Such, then, are some of the manuscript herbals, the majority of which antedate the introduction of printing. For the most part they are known to specialists only, and have therefore been allotted more space in this book than might otherwise seem to be justified. We turn now to the more familiar printed herbals, which made a somewhat tardy and unimpressive first appearance towards the close of the fifteenth century.

Badianus Herbal
Santa Cruz, 1552
Written in Latin
20.6 × 15.2 cm (8$\frac{1}{8}$ × 6 in)
62 folios
Biblioteca Apostolica Vaticana, Vatican, Codex Barberini Lat. 241
Colour plate p.110 'Marvel of Peru' (*Mirabilis jalapa*) and other plants, f14v.

1 E. W. Emmart (1940)

Badianus Herbal
Italy, 1626–7
Written in Latin
33.5 × 24 cm (13$\frac{1}{4}$ × 9$\frac{1}{2}$ in)
41 folios
Royal Library, Windsor
RL 27902-27938
Colour plate p.111 *Sedum dendroidum, Distichlis spicata, Datura arborea?, Mimosa* sp.? and 'sleep herb', f7r.

Opposite
Badianus Herbal, Vatican, top row, 'Painted tree', 'Tomato shrub' (*Arbutus* sp.), 'Bright tree', 'Sour tree' (*Conostegia? xalapensis*), 'Pleasant tree'; bottom row, 'Greatly honoured tree', 'Wild humming-bird flower', 'Maize flower', 'Popcorn flower' (*Bourreria huanita*) and 'Precious ylin', f39r.

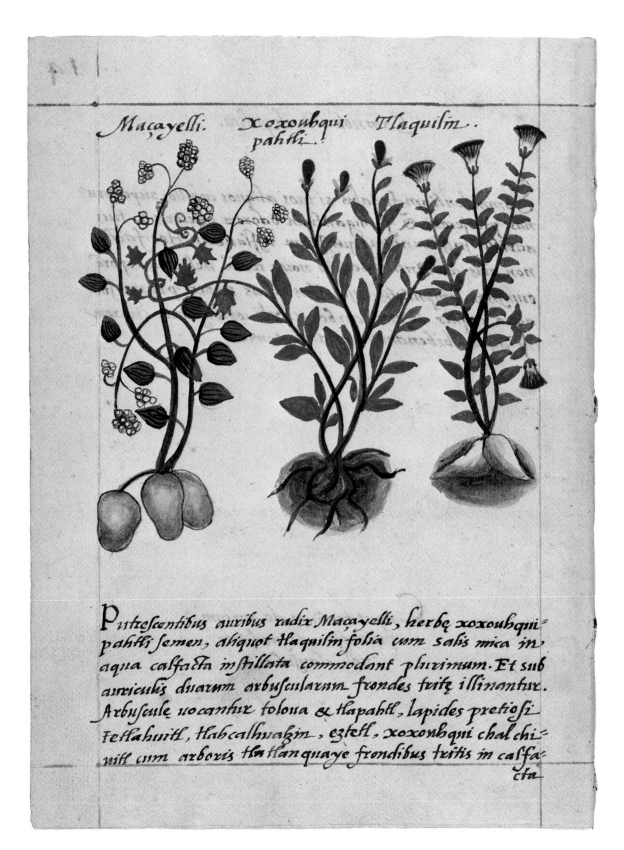

Maçayelli.   Xoxouhqui   Tlaquilin.
                pahtli.

Putrescentibus auribus radix Maçayelli, herbę xoxouhqui
pahtli femen, aliquot tlaquilin folia cum salis mica in
aqua calfacta instillata commodant plurimum. Et sub
auriculis duarum arbuscularum frondes tritę illinantur.
Arbusculę uocantur tolova & tlapahtl, lapides pretiosi
Teflahuitl, Hlabcalhuazin, eztetl. xoxouhqui chalchi=
uitl cum arboris tlatlanquaye frondibus tritis in calfa=
cta

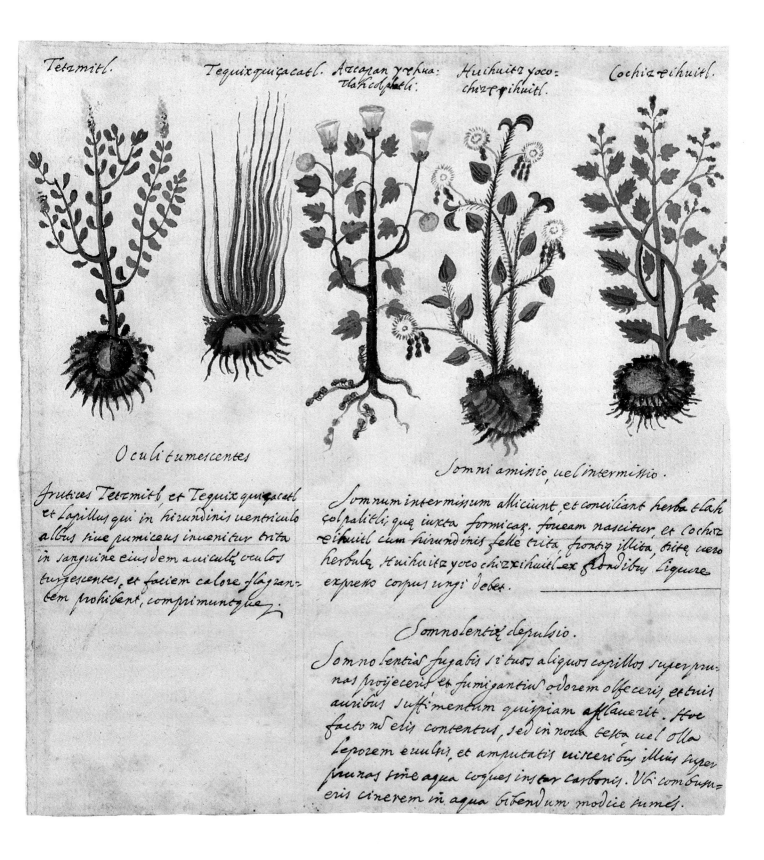

Tetzmitl. Tequixquiçacatl. Atzapan yxpua: Huihuitz yoco= Cochiztzihuitl.
tlahcolpahtli: chiztzpihuitl.

Oculi tumescentes

Somni amissio, vel intermissio.

Frutices Tetzmitl, et Tequixquiçacatl
et Capillus qui in hirundinis ventriculo
albus sive pumiceus invenitur trita
in sanguine eiusdem aviculæ oculos
turgescentes, et faciem calore flagran-
tem prohibent, comprimuntque.

Somnum intermissum alliciunt, et conciliant herba tlah
colpahtli, quæ iuxta formicas foveam nascitur, et Cochiz
zihuitl cum hirundinis felle trita, frontiq́ illita, vite vero
herbulæ Huihuitz yoco chiztzihuitl ex frondibus liquore
expresso corpus ungi debet.

Somnolentiæ depulsio.

Somnolentias fugabis si tuos aliquos capillos super prunas projeceris et fumigantium odorem olfeceris, et tuis
auribus suffimentum quispiam afflaverit. Hoc
facto nd elis contentus, sed in nova testa vel olla
leporem evulsis, et amputatis visceribus illius super
prunas sine aqua coques instar carbonis. Ubi combuss-
eris cinerem in aqua bibendum modice sumes.

The Woodcut Herbals

Humble Beginnings

'Xylograph', unlike 'lithograph', is a word 'now used only by bibliographers' – and not, indeed, always by them; in common parlance we speak of 'woodcut' or 'wood-engraving', making – as will be explained in a moment – a distinction between the two. For the Germans, usually so precise, *Holzschnitt* is made to serve for both, though they very sensibly avoid the ambiguity of our 'woodcutter', which can, of course, also mean 'tree-feller'.

In view of the fact that engraved seals date back more than six thousand years, it is surely astonishing that the earliest printing from wood-blocks is not to be found until the ninth century AD (in China), and in Europe not until the beginning of the fifteenth century, when it may have been introduced from the East or discovered independently. How is it possible that an idea so simple that a child might have stumbled upon it eluded great minds in the West for so long?

Megenberg *Půch der Natur* (1482 ed.) Lily-of-the-valley, violet, buttercup and other plants, f191r.

112

Woodcuts and wood-engravings are impressions on paper taken from a flat piece of wood, inked with a roller after what is superfluous to the design has been cut away. Basically, the woodcut is a black-line drawing. It is carried out on the plank of a soft wood, cherry for example, the background being removed with a knife. The wood-engraving is a white-line drawing; the line is incised with a gouge into the end-grain of a hard, fine-grained wood such as box or yew. Thomas Bewick (1753–1828) was one of the first great exponents of wood-engraving, availing himself to the full of the increased delicacy this technique allowed. Yet astonishing refinement was achieved by the woodcutters who worked for some of the later sixteenth-century European botanists, and in the eighteenth century by Japanese artists of the *ukiyo-e* such as Harunobu and Utamaro.

The first herbal illustrated with woodcuts dates from soon after the year 1480, by which time naturalism had already established itself not only in most other forms of art but even, as we have already seen, in the manuscript herbal. None the less, incunabula herbals and those of the first thirty years of the sixteenth century almost without exception perpetuated the crude, stylized and derivative figures of a remote past.

In 1475 there was published by Hans Bämler in Augsburg the so-called *Pũch der Natur* of Konrad von Megenberg (1309–98). Though not strictly a herbal, it contains a short section on plants illustrated with the first two botanical woodcuts ever made, and has a further claim to fame as the earliest work of its kind in the vernacular. A second edition appeared in 1482 in which the designs have been reversed, and it is interesting to observe that several of the leaves in two of the plants have now been treated more in the spirit of a wood-*engraving* than of a wood*cut* – that is to say, as black with white veinings.[1] This is unusual.

Though the plants in the *Pũch der Natur* are not very convincing botanically, they are far more naturalistic than those figured in what is generally considered to be the first herbal proper with printed illustrations: the *Herbal of Apuleius Platonicus*[2] (Rome, 1481?; not later than 1483). Johann Philippus de Lignamine, its editor and printer, was physician to Pope Sixtus IV.

We have already, when discussing manuscripts of this work, mentioned a ninth-century codex, formerly in the monastery of Monte Cassino destroyed by bombardment in 1944, that was the principal source of the *editio princeps*. Hunger's fine facsimile of the two works enables us to compare them page by page, and to observe that though there are striking similarities in many of the childish figures in both, there are also marked differences. We reproduce the 'Nepite' (*Nepeta cataria*, or catmint), which includes a serpent to indicate to the illiterate that it is recommended as an antidote to snake-bite; but even were the plant to be identified from this crude little picture, it is unlikely that it would afford much relief against snake venom. Infusion of the leaves of catmint is, however, still advocated by herbalists today, and Gerard (1597) commended it as 'a present helpe for them that be bursten inwardly, by meanes of some fall received from an high place, and that are very much bruised, if the juice be given with wine or meade'.

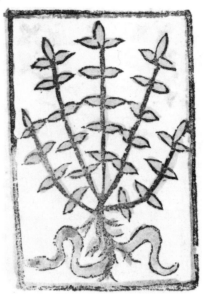

Apuleius Platonicus *Herbarium* Catmint (*Nepeta cataria*), f80r.

1 For an illustration of the woodcut as it appears in the 1475 edition see Arber (1986), plate iii, opp. p.14, and Anderson (1977), p.75.

2 It should be mentioned that these early printed herbals are usually known by innumerable different names – in this case, for example, *De Medicaminibus Herbarum Liber Uno, Herbarius Apulei Platonici, Herbarium de Sextus Apuleius Barbarus, Herbarium Apuleius Plato* and *De Herbarum Virtutibus*. The name of the author also occurs in various forms. We shall in general strictly ration our use of these alternatives.

1 Arber (1986), p.39.

In manuscripts of Apuleius the carrying of a sprig of artemisia (wormwood) was recommended as a specific against the weariness and dangers of travel in wild and mountainous country, and Arber[1] quotes an example of the persistence of belief in its alleged virtues: 'As recently as 1925, it was recorded that a driver of the "Auto-Post", on a precipitous road with hairpin bends leading to Maloja, was observed to have a branch of this plant hanging from his windscreen.'

It has been suggested that the figures in the printed *Herbal of Apuleius* may have been made from metal plates, not wooden blocks. Some of them certainly show a granular texture more characteristic of cast metal than of wood; others, however, do not. Unless the plates or blocks chance to be discovered, which is highly unlikely, the matter will probably never be settled.

A contender for the honour of being the first printed herbal with illustrations is the *De Viribus Herbarum* of Macer Floridus (Milan, 1482); an unillustrated edition, published in Naples in 1477, is certainly the earliest printed herbal.

2 (1977), p. 32.

Anderson[2] complains of the neglect of Macer's book by most writers on herbals; but he is not able to throw much light on its nebulous author. The text – which, he adds, 'differs from all other herbals because it is set in Latin verses [hexameters]' – describes the medicinal properties of a variety of plants, the number varying in different editions. Most of the material is derived from Pliny, and there is an unillustrated manuscript, now in Vienna, which dates from the eleventh century.

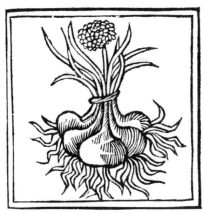

Macer *De Viribus Herbarum* Onions (*Allium cepa*), f27r.

The three remaining important incunabula herbals were all published in Mainz: the *Latin Herbarius* (Peter Schöffer, 1484), the *German Herbarius* or *Gart der Gesundheit* (Peter Schöffer, 1485) and the *Hortus* (or *Ortus*) *Sanitatis* (Jacob Meydenbach, 1491). Schöffer was Gutenberg's associate and successor, and inherited his presses and type. There is in addition the *Arbolayre*, also called *Le Grant Herbier* – a rare French work printed by Pierre Metlinger at Besançon *c.* 1486–8, with illustrations for the most part taken from those in the 1486 edition of the *German Herbarius*; it appeared in 1526 in an English translation entitled *The Grete Herball*.[3]

3 See p.163.

The bibliography of the early woodcut herbals, of which there were innumerable editions and translations, is one of almost unbelievable complexity and of small interest to the general reader.

The *Latin Herbarius* is possibly a miscellany made a century or so earlier than its first printing, though no manuscript of that period has as yet come to light.

The book – a small quarto with text largely borrowed from the *Speculum* of Vincent of Beauvais (d. *c.* 1260) – is divided into two major sections, the first giving figures and descriptions of 150 plants native to or cultivated in Germany. They are arranged alphabetically by their Latin names, with their German names added. Eleven incunabula editions have been recorded, that printed in Vicenza in 1491, which has a different set of figures, being sometimes wrongly described as the work of Arnaldus de Villa Nova. The illustrations of the *editio princeps*, while a considerable advance on those in the *Herbal of Apuleius*, are for the most part symmetrical and show little understanding of the structure of the plants. They are certainly decorative, though in some cases little more than diagrams and clearly not made direct from nature; but their source is not known.

Among the best are, perhaps, the fuller's teasel (*Dipsacus fullonum*) and the iris (*Iris pseudacorus*); yet only by its leaves can the latter be distinguished from the lily (*Lilium candidum*). Attractive, too, is the bryony (*Bryonia dioica*), which is reminiscent of plants used in the borders of medieval manuscripts.

At Kew there is a copy of the *Latin Herbarius* coloured by a contemporary hand. Some of the incunabula and sixteenth-century herbals were undoubtedly intended to be coloured, and in certain cases copies were issued in this state by the printer-publishers. Where the printed figure is in pure line or only minimally shaded, *good* colour, based on a specimen provided by the artist himself, can be very effective; but the later and more elaborately shaded herbals are often preferable in black and white. All herbals coloured by their owners lose a good deal of their beauty in the process, and modern colouring of course ruins them. Yet that the possessor of a herbal was often intended, even encouraged, to get to work with his paint-box is fairly certain, and in a famous early florilegium with metal-engraved plates, the *Hortus Floridus* of Crispin van de Pas (1614), detailed instructions are given of the colours required.

Within a year of the publication of the *Latin Herbarius*, Schöffer produced what is indisputably the most splendid and important of the incunabula herbals, the *German Herbarius*. It must have already been in preparation for a considerable time when the earlier herbal (of which it is not a mere translation) appeared, but the immediate and sensational success of the *Latin Herbarius* no doubt speeded up its publication.

The book is memorable in several ways. It was one of the first incunabula on a scientific subject written in the vernacular – in this case a Bavarian German none too easy to read. Then it is a folio, with figures considerably larger and more numerous than those in the *Latin Herbarius*. But what is of far greater interest to

Acorus Gellilien
Acorus calidus est et sic. in te͂bo. babet virtute͂ diuretica͂ dissolutiua absterfiua͂ ꝛ apitiua· Aco‑ rus ergo v; ad dissoluēdu͂ duricie splenis·et v; cōtra opilatione͂ splenis et epatis ex ca frigida ;puenientem·isto mo͂ dispensanto·ꝶ· radicem acori cōquassati quarta·lb·bumectetur radix in aceto ad tres dies cui adde radice͂ reupontici·ʒ·ij floꝛu͂ boraginis stolopendrie an·m·ꝗ· seminis

Brionia roselwurzel
brionia est calide et sicce ōplexionis sc; tota ber‑ ba sc; folia fructus ꝛ radix et habent virtute͂ abstergendi et subtiliandi ꝛ dissoluēdi sc͂o va‑ lent in duricie splenis faciendo emplastrum ex eo et radice altee et ficub; cu͂ aqua tꝛcoquēbo cu͂ auxūgia porci ꝛ loco indurato ipius splenis ap‑ plicando vel alio membro indura to et valebit Ite͂m cu͂ succo brionie abraditur pili coriorum·

Far left
Latin Herbarius Iris (*Iris pseudacorus*), cap. iiii.

Left
Latin Herbarius Bryony (*Bryonia dioica*), cap. xxxi.

us is that a number of these figures – perhaps as many as 65 of the 379 – appear to have been drawn from the actual plants, the inaccuracies of detail observable in some of them being very likely the fault rather of a crude woodcutter than of the artist himself. And, lastly, the work is provided with splendid indexes.

The preface opens with a noble paean to the Creator – a hymn of praise such as so often precedes the works of devout Muslim authors:

> Many a time and oft have I bethought within myself of the wondrous works of the Shaper of the Universe . . . While considering these matters I likewise recalled the Shaper of Nature, Who has set us amidst such perils, has granted us a remedy with all manner of herbs, animals, and sundry other created things . . . I thank Thee, O Shaper of heaven and earth . . . that Thou has granted to me grace of revealing this treasure, which has until now lain hidden and buried from the sight of common men.[1]

Some of these 'common men' were quick off the mark to take advantage of this potential gold-mine and, the law of copyright apparently being ill-defined or non-existent,[2] produced pirated editions of the *German Herbarius*. Johann (Hanns) Schönsperger of Augsburg had the book in print (with reversed figures) within five months, and by 1502 had published no less than eight further editions. Other plagiarists soon joined in, with the result that in addition to the *editio princeps*, thirteen incunabula editions – all similarly illustrated though often with smaller figures – exist, the remainder coming from presses in Strasbourg, Basel, Ulm and Lübeck.

The book, as we learn from its preface, was put together by a wealthy amateur who received medical advice from a certain Johann von Cube, who names himself in chapter 76 and has been identified with Dr Johann Wonnecke, of Caub or Cube, town physician of Frankfurt am Main at that time. The compiler, observing while work was in progress that many of the herbs mentioned by the ancients did not grow in Germany, set out on a spiritual-botanical pilgrimage to the Holy Land, eventually travelling as far as Mount Sinai. He writes:

> In order that the noble work I had begun and left unfinished should not come to nothing, and also that my journey should not benefit my soul only, but the whole world, I took with me a painter of good sense, skilful and cunning . . . In wandering through these kingdoms and countries, I diligently sought after the herbs there, and had them drawn and depicted in their true forms and colours.

So long a journey confirms that work on the *German Herbarius* must have been in progress several years before the publication of the *Latin Herbarius*. It is tempting to identify the anonymous author of the former and the painter who accompanied him on his journey with Bernhard von Breydenbach and his artist fellow-traveller Erhard Rewich, who made the same pilgrimage at about the same time; but this has been shown to be impossible.[3] Such journeys, in spite of the trouble, hardships and dangers involved, were not uncommon in those days.

The two indexes to the *German Herbarius* were 'far in advance

1 Anderson (1977), p.96. Arber (1986), p.23, quotes the preface almost *in extenso*, using a translation made by E. G. Tucker.

2 Yet not very long afterwards a successful action was brought in a similar case (see p.123).

3 Payne (1901), p.95.

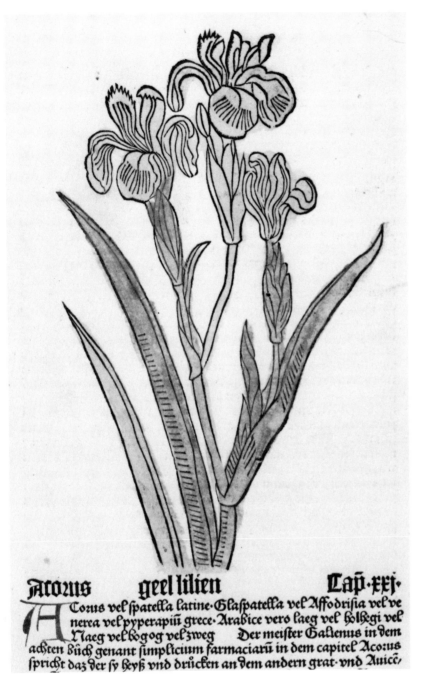

Acorus   geel lilien   Cap·xxi·
ACorus vel ſpatella latine·Glaſpatella vel Affodriſia vel ve
nerea vel pyperapiū grece· Arabice vero laeg vel holßegi vel
Naeg vel bogog vel zweg   Der meiſter Galienus in dem
achten Buch genant ſimplicium farmaciarū in dem capitel Acorus
ſpricht das der ſy heyß vnd drücken an dem andern grat· vnd Auicē/

German Herbarius Iris (*Iris pseudacorus*), cap. xxi.

of those that were compiled during the following four or five decades'.[1] The first dealt with diseases and other miscellaneous matters, 'so that you, dearest reader, may prevail to find quickly in this work what you require and what remedy of an illness you ought to apply.' The last entries, listed in no apparent order, are:

1 Wellisch (1978), p.84.

How to make your guests gay and happy.
When you want to know whether a sick person will die or recover.
When the skin of young children is flaking off under the arms.
How to remove spots caused by the sun.
What kills rats.
To remove the worms that are stuck into the sweatholes of young children.

There follows an index of plants, arranged alphabetically (by the

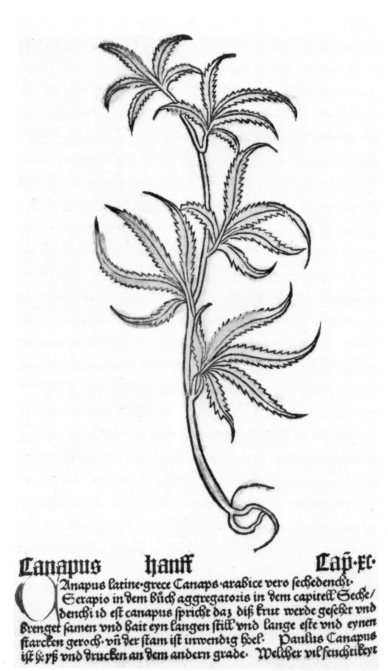

Canapus   hanff   Cap·rc·

Canapus latine·grece Canaps·arabice vero fechedenchi·
Serapio in dem buch aggregatoris in dem capitell Seche/
denchi id eſt canapus ſpricht daʒ diß krut werde geſetʒt vnd
brenget ſamen vnd bait eyn langen ſtill vnd lange eſte vnd eynen
ſtarcken geroch· vn̄ der ſtam iſt inwendig hoel·   Paulus Canapus
iſt heyß vnd drucken an dem andern grade·   Welcher vil feuchtikeyt

German Herbarius Cannabis
(*Cannabis sativa*), cap. xc.

first letter only) according to their Latin names, together with
their German equivalents.

Among the most attractive of the woodcuts clearly made from
nature are those of the yellow flag (*Iris pseudacorus*), winter
cherry (*Physalis alkekengi*) and columbine (*Aquilegia* sp.). There
is also a good picture of '*Canapus* or *Hanff*' (*Cannabis sativa*) – our
'pot', 'marijuana', etc. This was prescribed 'for distended
stomachs, dropsy, pains in the anal region, and as a plaster for
boils and carbuncles. Applied to wounds it relieved pain, and a
decoction of its roots and seeds mixed with white lead and roses
was used to treat erysipelas. Only when its vapours were
employed to ease headache did it come close to its modern use as a
hallucinogen.'[1] Even the derivative figures in this noble work are
superior to those in the *Latin Herbarius*.

The *Hortus Sanitatis* of 1491 – a folio with more than a thousand
(mostly small) woodcuts – is certainly an impressive book, but it

1 Anderson (1977), p.94.

118

is far more medieval in character than the *German Herbarius* of six years earlier. Its scope, however, is wider, for it includes sections dealing with fish, birds and other animals, and one on minerals. The text is, as usual, a compilation, part of it being drawn from that of the *German Herbarius*.

The majority of its 530 botanical illustrations are copied – crudely, on a reduced scale, and occasionally reversed – from those in the *German Herbarius*. Of the new figures, some of those of native plants are tolerably naturalistic; the remainder are partly or wholly fanciful, among these being the well-known narcissus, which shows an engaging survival of the classical legend and would be more at home in the *Nonsense Botany* of Edward Lear.[1] The 'Ligusticum' (lovage, *Levisticum officinale*) is one of a number of woodcuts enlivened by extraneous material, in this case a neat little Gothic church.

1 Blunt (1950), p.41.

It might at first sight seem that a chapter on the early printed herbals should stop at 1500, the terminal year of the incunabulum. But it was in 1530, with the publication by Schott of Strasbourg of the first volume of Brunfels's *Herbarum Vivae Eicones*, that the logical break came, for the first three decades of the sixteenth century were stagnant where the development of botanical illustration in the printed herbal was concerned.

The continent of Europe provided nothing new; Banckes's *Herball*, the first such work in English, is not illustrated; and though there is a woodcut of herbs and trees in Wynkyn de Worde's edition (*c.* 1495) of that encyclopaedia of the Middle Ages, the *Liber de Proprietatibus Rerum* of Bartholomaeus Anglicus, it hardly warrants inclusion in this book. The figures of *The Grete Herball* (1526) are the same as those of *Le Grant Herbier*, which were in any case derived from the usual sources; in a later chapter we will say something further of this popular book. It may, however, be of interest to note that in this dark half-century, and indeed even earlier, the Chinese were producing herbals with woodcuts of far greater botanical accuracy and distinction than anything to be found in Europe.

1 Vol. 2, 1532; vol. 3, 1536. But
according to W. L. Schreiber (1924),
both volumes 1 and 2 'probably first
appeared in 1532, though the Preface
to the former is dated 1530 and that
to the latter 1531.'
2 See colour plates pp.131, 134–35.
3 A notable exception is James
Sowerby's *English Botany*
(1790–1814), whose author, Sir
James Edward Smith, modestly did
not even allow his name to appear in
the first number issued.

The Golden Age

Where botanical illustration is concerned, the opening of a new era dates, as we have already said, from the publication in 1530 of the first volume of Brunfels's *Herbarum Vivae Eicones*[1] – the first such work to be illustrated throughout with, as its title tells us, 'living portraits of plants': what we should today call 'plants drawn from nature'.[2]

It is a misfortune only too common in illustrated botanical works for the name of the author to have eclipsed that of the artist.[3] Of this unhappy tendency Otto Brunfels is a notable example. Though sometimes hailed by his compatriots as one of the pioneers of modern botany, Brunfels was in fact little more than another of those industrious gleaners of miscellaneous material, chiefly from the well-worn pages of what he himself termed 'ancient and trustworthy authors', seasoned with snippets from more recent Italian sources. The proud claim made in his preface – 'I have no other aim than that of giving a prop to fallen botany: to bring back life to a science almost extinct' – was not realized. His text, however, was, as he proclaimed, to be illustrated with 'new and really lifelike figures'; but since he still tried to identify his plants with those of Dioscorides, ignoring the fact that the flora of the eastern Mediterranean was different from that of the Rhineland, this naturally resulted in much confusion.

We may deal with Brunfels briefly. He was born near Mainz in 1489, and no doubt his interest in botany was aroused, or at all events further stimulated, by knowledge of the three famous incunabula published in that city: the *Latin Herbarius*, the *German Herbarius* and the *Hortus Sanitatis*. After some years in a Carthusian monastery he became in 1521 a convert to Lutheranism, and finally settled down as a schoolmaster and preacher in Strasbourg, where he wrote several theological works intended, no doubt, to give a prop to fallen religion. In 1532 he was appointed town physician in Bern. His *Herbarum Vivae Eicones*, the third volume of which did not appear until two years after his death, must be considered as the product of his leisure hours.

Happily, Hans Weiditz seems soon to have become the dominant force in the production of this herbal – something for which, though it irked Brunfels, posterity is grateful. Dr Arber writes:

> Brunfels regarded the classical names of herbs as the *real* names, and he had intended to relegate to a mere appendix those plants which could not claim to have been sponsored by antiquity, and were so luckless as to possess vernacular names alone. He called these poor things *herbae nudae*, forlorn or destitute herbs. His neat plan for thus separating the sheep from the goats was, however, dislocated, because Weiditz and his assistants insisted on drawing what they chose when they chose, and their choice sometimes fell upon these botanical outcasts; so that – with the printer waiting for copy – Brunfels was faced with the inclusion of pictures of upstart plants, unknown to the ancients, which he had had no intention of honouring in this way.[4]

Poor Brunfels felt obliged on several occasions to apologize to his readers for this lapse – for example, when mentioning the

4 Arber (1953), p.323.

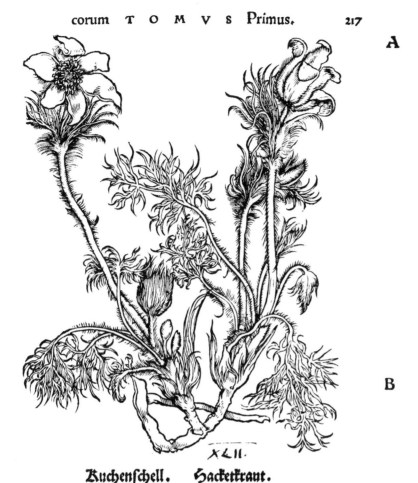

A

B

XLII.

Kuchenſchell.   Hackerkraut.

OTHO BRVNNFELSIVS.

ONSTITVERAMVS ab ipſo ſtatim operis noſtri initio,
quicquid eſſet huiuſcemodi herbarum incognitarum, et de qua*
im nomenclaturis dubitaremus, ad libri calcem appendere, & eas tan=
im ſumere deſcribendas, quæ fuiſſent plane uulgatiſſimæ, adeoq; & of
cinis in uſu: uerum longe ſecus accidit, & rei ipſius periculum nos edo*
ιit, interdum ſeruiendum eſſe ſcenæ καὶ καιρῶ λατρευειν, quod dicitur. Nam
ιm formarum deliniatores & ſculptores, uehementer nos remoraren=
ιr, ne interim ocioſe agerent & pręla, coacti ſumus, quamlibet proxime
buiam arripere. Statuimus igitur nudas herbas, quarum tantum nomi
a germanica nobis cognita ſunt, pręterea nihil. Nam latina necg; ab me=
icis, necg; ab herbarijs rimari ualuimus (tantum abeſt, ut ex Dioſcoride,
el aliquo ueterum hanc quiuerimus demonſtrare) magis adeo ut locum
ιpplerent, & occaſionem pręberent doctioribus de ijs deliberandi , &

t 3

Brunfels *Herbarum Vivae Eicones*
Pasque-flower (*Pulsatilla vulgaris*),
vol. I, p. 217.

pasque-flower (*Pulsatilla vulgaris*); little could he have guessed
that this exquisite woodcut, which he would have preferred to
exclude, would today be remembered for its beauty – and,
incidentally, as the original type picture of a Linnaean species.

Nonetheless, at the beginning of his work Brunfels did pay a
generous and well-deserved tribute to the artist responsible for
most if not all the drawings in the first two volumes, and
probably for cutting the wood-blocks also:

> Nunc & Johannes pictor Guidictius ille
>   Clarus Apellæo non minus ingenio,
> Reddedit at fabras æri sic arte figuras
>   Ut non nemo Herbas dixerit esse meras!

In other words, such was Weiditz's skill that no one could say, 'These plants are not real.' Indeed,

> a whole world separates these strong, well-observed drawings from even the best figures in the *German Herbarius* of 1485. We are reminded at once of Dürer; and much of Weiditz's work has in fact been falsely attributed at one time or another to that great master, or to Burgkmair. How vigorously the hellebore thrusts its leaf diagonally across the page; how exquisitely the hairy quality of the pasque-flower has been realised! The outline is never dull or mechanical. Though there is still present a certain Gothic angularity in the conception, there is tenderness too; we sense that strange admixture of severity and sweetness which gives to the Madonnas of medieval German art their peculiar charm . . .
>
> Weiditz accepted Nature as he found her. Was a leaf tattered or drooping, a flower withered? – he observed the fact with the cold eye of the realist and recorded it with the precision of a true craftsman. Yet beauty was never wantonly sacrificed to mere scientific accuracy; the poet in him always triumphed. His work must ever remain the high-water mark of woodcutting employed in the service of botanical illustration.[1]

If one should dare to criticize such a masterpiece, it would be to suggest that the combination of full-page woodcuts and small – even very small – figures scattered rather casually throughout the text is not wholly successful. This was an error that Fuchs, a decade later, was to avoid.

Seventy-seven lovely watercolour paintings by Weiditz,[2] which date from 1529, were discovered in an attic of the Bern Botanical Institute in 1930, where they had been incorporated in the herbarium of the Basel naturalist Felix Platter. The lucky finder, Walther Rytz, published a full account of them in 1933, and subsequently a number of excellent colour plates of a selection of them.[3] Unhappily Weiditz used both sides of the paper – a luckless economy 'which led the methodical Platter to mangle the drawings cruelly in order to stick them into the appropriate place in his collection.'[4]

It is interesting to compare Weiditz's paintings with the woodcuts made from them, the former being clearly intended to serve as a guide for the colouring of a number of copies of the herbal issued in that state by the publisher. In certain cases, modifications have had to be made – by Weiditz, or by his assistant engraver – in order to accommodate the bigger drawings to the printed page. Further, while it is in general possible to judge with reasonable certainty whether or not the colouring of a woodcut herbal is contemporary or relatively modern, whether issued in that state by the publisher, or coloured by an amateur purchaser, the Weiditz originals establish beyond doubt that the coloured copy of Brunfels at Kew is authentic.

A German translation, in folio, of the first two volumes of Brunfels, entitled *Contrafayt Kreüterbůch*, was issued in 1532, and a second volume was published posthumously in 1537; these included nearly all the figures of the Latin version, and more than fifty additional ones.[5]

1 Blunt (1950), p.47.

2 See colour plate p.130.

3 See Rytz (1933) and (1936).

4 Arber (1986), p.206. This is a regrettable habit of botanists devoid of aesthetic feeling – see, for example, Blunt (1950) p.237 for the fate of Moggridge's lovely paintings of flowers of the Riviera, snipped by a Kew botanist into tiny pieces for the same purpose.

5 For a detailed account of Brunfels, see Sprague (1928).

In 1533, Eucharius Rhodion (better known as Rösslin) issued in Frankfurt am Main, where he was town physician, a *Kreutterbůch* most of whose figures were lifted from Brunfels, then reduced and reversed. Schott sued Egenolph, Rösslin's publisher, for piracy – apparently with success, for the blocks were recovered and used by Schott in the following year in a quarto edition of the *Herbarum Vivae Eicones*.

Rösslin published his book before the third part of Brunfels had appeared; he was therefore obliged to plunder from other sources as well, including archaic figures from several incunabula.

The *De Historia Stirpium*, published by Isingrin of Basel in 1542 and a year later in a German translation entitled *New Kreüterbůch*,[1] is a folio of breathtaking splendour.

1 A facsimile of this edition was published in Munich in 1964.

Its author, Leonhart Fuchs, was born at Wemding, in Bavaria, in 1501, and such was his precocity that at the age of sixteen he opened a school of his own in his native city. Two years later, however, conscious that he himself still had much to learn, he went to Ingolstadt University to study the classics and philosophy, and subsequently medicine. By 1524 he was a Master of Arts and a Doctor of Medicine, and, through reading the works of Martin Luther, had become an ardent Protestant. Details of his medical career in Munich, Ingolstadt, and Ansbach (where he became famous for his treatment of victims of a plague known as the 'English Sweating Sickness') must be read elsewhere.[2] In 1535 we find him professor of medicine at Tübingen, where he was to spend the remaining thirty-one years of his life.

2 See Sprague and Nelmes (1931).

Though Fuchs railed against the botanical ignorance of the medical men of his day, alleging that it was 'almost impossible to find even one in a hundred who has any accurate knowledge of even a few plants', much of his own text was derived from Dioscorides. He also owed something to Brunfels and even more to the *New Kreütter Bůch* (1539) of Hieronymus Bock – a book to which we shall refer later, since the first edition with illustrations did not appear until 1546. But Fuchs was a better scholar than either of these men, though far from Bock's equal as an observer; and the accusation sometimes made against him that he was merely an armchair botanist is unjust, as is made clear by what he wrote in his preface:

> But there is no reason why I should dilate at greater length upon the pleasantness and delight of acquiring knowledge of plants, since there is no one who does not know that there is nothing in this life pleasanter and more delightful than to wander over woods, mountains, plains, garlanded and adorned with flowerlets and plants of various sorts, and most elegant to boot, and to gaze intently upon them. But it increases that pleasure and delight not a little, if there is added an acquaintance with the virtues and powers of these same plants.[3]

3 Translated by Arber (1986), p.67.

That Fuchs was a field botanist is further evinced by various asides in his herbal. For example, it was he who first recorded – no doubt from personal experience – that the sap of the celery-leaved buttercup (*Ranunculus sceleratus*) burned the skin, and was used for this purpose by 'roguish beggars, who ought to be

PICTORES OPERIS,
Heinricus Füllmaurer.   Albertus Meyer.

SCVLPTOR
Vitus Rodolph. Speckle.

Fuchs *De Historia Stirpium* Albrecht
Meyer, Heinrich Füllmaurer and Veit
Rudolf Speckle, opp. p. 896.

1 See colour plates pp. 142–43.

packed off to the devil' to produce bogus sores to deceive the
innocent compassionate. However, Sprague and Nelmes are no
doubt right in describing Fuchs the botanist as 'an industrious,
methodical, and judicious compiler, rather than an investigator'.

Our principal concern with Fuchs's *De Historia Stirpium* is of
course with its illustrations.[1] The great folio is provided with
more than five hundred full-page woodcuts of plants, preceded
by a portrait of the author in doctor's robes and closing with
others of the artists whose work so substantially contributed to
the book's fame and beauty: Albrecht Meyer, who drew the
plants from nature; Heinrich Füllmaurer, an artist who also
transferred the drawings to the blocks; and Veit Rudolf Speckle,
who did the cutting. This was a handsome tribute to his skilful
collaborators. Meyer is shown at work upon a highly incompetent drawing of a corn-cockle – a fact which has given rise to
the suggestion that Füllmaurer and Speckle may perhaps have
been having a joke at his expense.

Margaret Marcus,[1] in making a comparison between the figures in Brunfels and Fuchs, is of the opinion that in the majority of cases 'the outlines [of the former] lack the vibrancy and elegance of Fuchs's work.' Admittedly a first glance might lead one to suppose that almost everything favoured the superiority of the latter:

1 Marcus (1944), p.381.

> We are dazzled by Fuchs's splendid folio pages; by his crisp, white paper; by his spacious designs; by the fine printing and lay-out of the book, and by the sheer quantity of the illustrations – more than twice as many as those in Brunfels. When we further recollect that this book was to have been but the first of three similar volumes, it is impossible not to admit the magnitude and daring of his conception and the importance of what he actually achieved. But it must not be forgotten that Brunfels was the pioneer. Weiditz's noble full-page drawings of water-lilies – which Fuchs's artists did not even attempt to better, but adapted rather clumsily to their own purpose – gave a lead which was eagerly followed, but set a standard which was not to be surpassed.[2]

2 Blunt (1950), p.49.

If the contours of the cuts in Fuchs's herbal seem rather too thin to support a drawing in pure outline, we must remember that his plates were intended to be coloured. A number of such copies have in fact survived, and their uniformity confirms that they were issued in this state by the publisher. The author, as he explains in his preface, was particularly anxious that no shading should disturb the clarity of the figures:

> As far as concerns the pictures themselves, each of which is positively delineated according to the features and likeness of the living plants, we have taken peculiar care that they should be most perfect; and, moreover, we have devoted the greatest diligence to secure that every plant should be depicted with its own roots, stalks, leaves, flowers, seeds and fruits. Furthermore, we have purposely and deliberately avoided the obliteration of the natural form of the plants by shadows, and other less necessary things, by which the delineators sometimes try to win artistic glory: and we have not allowed the craftsmen so to indulge their whims as to cause the drawing not to correspond accurately to the truth. Veit Rudolf Speckle, by far the best engraver in Strasbourg, has admirably copied the wonderful industry of the draughtsmen, and has with such excellent craft expressed in his engraving the features of each drawing, that he seems to have contended with the draughtsmen for glory and victory.

In fact, Fuchs held his team of artists on a much tighter rein than did Brunfels, and as always happens in such cases the work, though it may benefit scientifically, inevitably suffers aesthetically. Weiditz was a great artist who, like Dürer, approached nature with humility; Meyer was no more than a fairly competent draughtsman, ready (or obliged) to bow to a botanist's whims. He idealized his plants as the Greek sculptors idealized their portraits, for, as Arber observes, the drawing that is perfect from the standpoint of systematic botany 'avoids the accidental peculiarities of any individual species'. Hence she, too, prefers

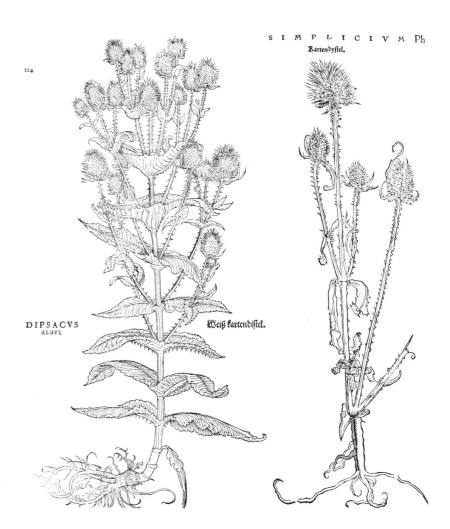

SIMPLICIVM Ph

Bartendyftel.

224

DIPSACVS
ALBVS.

Weiß fartendiftel.

Far right
Brunfels *Herbarum Vivae Eicones*
Teasel (*Dipsacus fullonum*), vol. II,
66.

Right
Fuchs *De Historia Stirpium* Teasel
(*Dipsacus fullonum*), p. 224.

1 See colour plate p.139

the illustrations to Fuchs, in that they seek to express the character and habit of a *species*, not of an individual, and usually imperfect, specimen.

The reader must judge for himself, and indeed bear in mind that both Ruskin and William Morris were proud to possess copies of Fuchs and loudly sang the praise of his artists. (But did they, one wonders, ever see Brunfels?) Take, for example, the figures of the fuller's teasel (*Dipsacus fullonum*) from the two works in question. Weiditz's plant is such as may be found in any hedgerow; for that of Meyer we must await the gardens, or hedgerows, of Paradise.

The best plates in Fuchs are very effective. The graceful fronds of the asparagus (*Asparagus sylvestris*) could hardly be bettered,[1] and the wild arum (*Arum maculatum*) has an admirable drawing of the fruit and a dissection. Climbing plants are sometimes represented as forming an all-over pattern which may well have inspired Morris wallpapers. But sometimes a tree bows its head or cringes rather too self-consciously in order to keep itself within the confines of the block, and either Meyer or his collaborators must have been nodding when they produced figures as clumsy as those of one or two of the geraniums. It was, however, economy which led to the use of a single plate to show a plant simultaneously flowering and fruiting, and to three distinct species of *Lamium* rising from a single root – a fact which copies of the herbal with contemporary colouring make plain. This practice dates back to the days of the *Codex Vindobonensis* of Dioscorides.

825

TVRCICVM
FRVMENTVM
Türckisch korn.

Fuchs *De Historia Stirpium* Maize
(*Zea mays*), p. 825.

Among the figures of especial interest in Fuchs is the first
representation of maize (*Zea mays*) in a herbal, though it had been
described three years earlier in the unillustrated edition of Bock
and had long since been reported upon by Spanish explorers of
the New World. An article which may perhaps not have come the
reader's way – 'Maize in the Great Herbals' by John J. Finan[1] –
describes in detail the story of this staple food of the American
Indians, which Fuchs, mistaking its country of origin, called
'Turcicum Frumentum', or Turkish corn.[2]

The article contains much fascinating information about maize
– for example, that the Aztecs worshipped a maize god; that the
Peruvians used it to make little communion wafers for sun-
worshipping ceremonies, and that the Nicaraguan Indians
(allegedly) refrained from sexual intercourse from the time of its
sowing to that of its harvesting. Oviedo's account (1535) of an
Aztec sacrificial maize ceremony is too revolting to quote here –
and, incidentally, too irrelevant.

What, however, is to our purpose is the description in certain
herbals of the colour of the kernel, which is variously reported as
existing in red, black, brown, blue, white, yellow and purple

1 Finan (1945).

2 *Cf.* the turkey – an American bird.

127

varieties. Gerard,[1] who used eight figures of maize from the *Neuw Kreuterbuch* (c. 1590) of Brunfels's pupil, Tabernaemontanus, wrote: 'The graine is of sundrie colours, sometimes red, and sometimes white, and yellow, as my selfe have seene in mine owne garden, where it hath come to ripenes.' Gerard had a low opinion of the value of maize as food: 'It doth nourish far lesse than either Wheate, Rie, Barly or Otes.' It produced bread almost as unappetising as that supplied by our bakers today – 'hard and dry as biskit is' – and was 'a more convenient food for swine than for men'. Parkinson,[2] quoting Acosta (1578), maintained that over-indulgence in maize 'engenders grosse blood, which breedeth itches and scabbes in those that were not used to it.' It seems strange that its economic importance received so little recognition at the time.

The folio editions of Fuchs were too expensive for the ordinary field botanist to buy and far too heavy (about 5 kg, 11 lb!) for him to take with him into the countryside. Soon, therefore, various smaller and pocket editions appeared, with freshly cut blocks, including an octavo with four figures to a page and no text (Basel, 1545) and finally even plump little duodecimos – what Edmund Gosse used to call 'dumpy twelves' – with a single figure to a page (Lyons, 1549, etc.). Of the miniature editions, that of 1555, exquisitely printed by Jean de Tournes, was less than 12.5 × 7.5 cm (5 × 3 in.). In them the plates, losing the thinness of line that mars those in the folios in an uncoloured state, actually gain in strength. Both Brunfels and Bock also appeared in smaller formats, and their blocks and texts, like Fuchs's, were endlessly pirated. An unillustrated edition of Fuchs was published in Hamburg in 1602, and use was made in Tübingen in 1739 of the figures from an earlier edition. The actual blocks of the *editio princeps* of Fuchs made their final bow in Salomon Schinz's *Anleitung zu der Pflanzenkenntniss* (Zürich, 1774).

A collection of drawings made for the first edition of Fuchs's *De Historia Stirpium*, and for two further volumes which he was never able to publish, is now in the Österreichische National-bibliothek in Vienna.[3]

It had always been assumed that this priceless treasure had vanished for ever[4]. On Fuchs's death it had passed to his son, then to a publisher in Ulm; but nothing had been heard of it since 1732, when a Viennese bookseller was offering it for sale at 300 gulden. Great, therefore, was the excitement when it suddenly came to light at a congress of the International League of Antiquarian Booksellers held in Vienna in 1954, and was acquired by the nation. It consists of some 1525 drawings – by Albrecht Meyer, Heinrich Füllmaurer, and at least one other artist – and is contained in nine folio volumes (pressmark Cod. 11117–11125).

The drawing of the greater celandine (*Chelidonium majus*) here reproduced,[5] presumably the work of Meyer, makes plain how much he owed to Füllmaurer and Speckle, and gives support to the theory that the jest about the corn-cockle was indeed barbed. It is interesting to note the three little hands with pointing fingers, just visible in the top lefthand corner of the drawing, that indicate the correct size of flowers and fruit which elsewhere the artist has made too small. This error was duly corrected.

1 *Herball* (1597), pp.74–7.

2 *Theatrum Botanicum* (1640), p.1139.

3 Ganzinger (1959).

4 Some drawings once believed to be the originals, now in the Department of Prints and Drawings of the British Library, are early and rather feeble copies.

5 See colour plate p.138.

128

Fuchs (meaning 'Fox') had, when need arose, not been embarrassed to use the Latinized form of his name, Fuchsius; Hieronymus Bock ('Jerome He-goat') preferred to disguise his by coining the Greco-Latin Tragus, though the pure Latin *caper* was already available; and it seems rather uncharitable of David Kandel, who was to illustrate the second edition of his *New Kreütter Büch*, to have surmounted his portrait of the author with a satyr's mask crowned with a goat's horns. This title-page is reproduced by Arber in her *Herbals* (p. 58).

Bock was born in 1498 at Heidelsheim, south of Heidelberg, and intended by his parents for a monastic life. He chose, however, to study medicine and was for a time a schoolmaster until at the age of twenty-five he was appointed by Count Palatine Ludwig to superintend his gardens. On the Count's death nine years later he became a Lutheran pastor at Hornbach, where, but for a troubled interlude in exile brought about by the Counter-Reformation, he remained until his own death in 1554. Bock was at one time of much assistance to Brunfels, who in his turn encouraged Bock to persevere with his botanical studies and eventually publish a book in the vernacular; but by the time it appeared, Brunfels had been dead for some years.

The great achievement of Bock – one in a field in which Brunfels and Fuchs were no rivals, and no progress had been made since the days of Theophrastus – was as a pioneer of descriptive botany (phytography). Brunfels's herbal had not sold well, and it was probably in part Bock's inability to persuade his publisher to pay for illustrations for the first edition of his *New Kreütter Büch* (1539) that obliged him to describe in detail (and in an almost cheekily colloquial German) facts that Brunfels and Fuchs mistakenly believed to have been adequately dealt with by their artists. There was, however, far more to it than that, and Arber[1] is particularly good on the quality of his achievements; but since we are concerned primarily with the illustrated herbal we can quote only a paragraph from what she wrote on the subject!

> When he described a plant, his ideal evidently was to give a concise account of the life-history, rather than to limit attention to the flowering epoch – a phase to which systematic descriptions are still too often confined. The stress which Bock lays on the developmental sequence from season to season of the year comes out conspicuously in what he says of the lesser celandine (*Ranunculus ficaria*). His description of the leaves and roots is adapted from Dioscorides, but his account of the flower and of the life-history is his own. He explains that the plant appears about the end of February, on moist hills, in vineyards, and in certain meadows, and is rendered conspicuous by its green hue. Like arum and the orchis kind, it comes to life afresh every year, with new roots, leaves and flower. A slender stalk shoots up, bearing a very beautiful yellow bloom, which clearly represents a little star, and recalls that of ranunculus. Withering in the month of May, it dies away, letting fall its leaves and flowers, the rootlets meanwhile lying hid in the earth until the beginning of February in the following year.[2]

1 (1953), p.326; and see also E. L. Greene (1983) for an excellent account of Bock.

2 (1953), p.326.

Colour plates
Page 130 Weiditz Purple and military orchids (*Orchis mascula*? and *O. militaris*).
Page 131 Brunfels *Herbarum Vivae Eicones* Daffodil (*Narcissus pseudo-narcissus*) and Spring snowflake (*Leucoium vernum*), p. 61. The contemporary colouring in this and the other two illustrations, on pp. 134 and 135, from the same copy has faded considerably over the years.

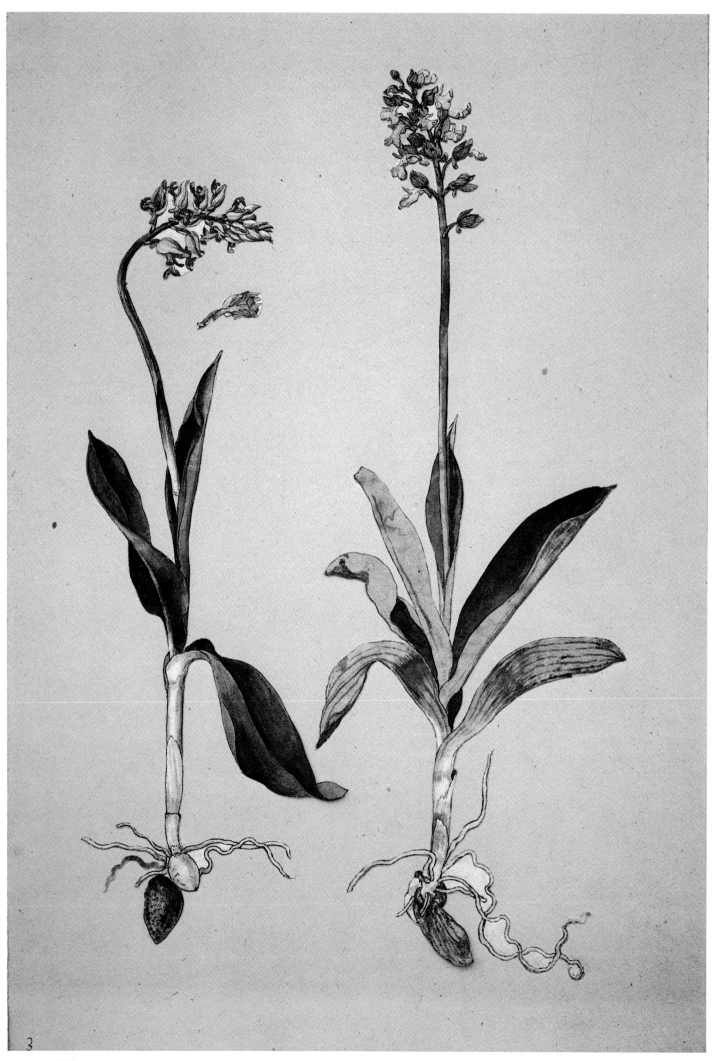

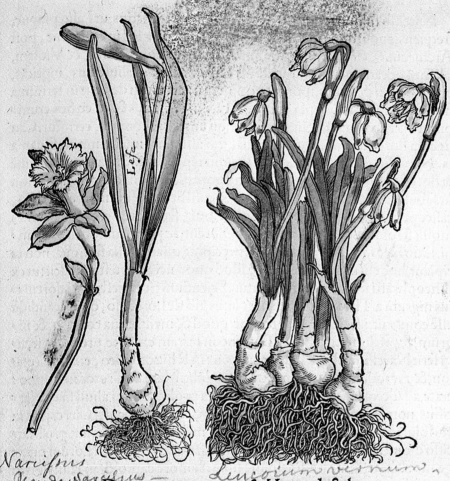

Narciſſus
Pſeudonarciſſus   *Leucoium vernum.*

DE NARCISSO, & Hermodactylo,
Rhapſodia Viceſima.

❡ NOMENCLATVRAE.

Græcæ, νάρκισσοσ. ἀυτογινίσ. βόλβοσ ὁ ἐμετικόσ. λίιριον. ἄνϋθρος.

Latinæ, Narciſſus, Hermodactylus.

Germanicę, in Marcio, **Hornungs blům**. In Septembri, **Zeytlőſlin**.

PLACITA AVTORVM de Narciſſo.

Hiſtoria Narciſſi, ſecundum DIO =

SCORIDEM, lib. ୨.

Narciſſvs folia Porro ſimillima habet, tenuia, multo mi=
nora, & anguſtiora: caulis uacuus, & ſine folijs, ſupra dodrantem attolli=
tur: flos albus in medio, intus croceus, in quibuſdam purpureus: radix in
tus alba, rotunda, bulboſa: ſemen uelut in tunica, nigrum, longum. Pro=
batiſſimum naſcitur in montibus ſuaui odore. Cætera Porrum imitatur,
atcɜ hærbaceum uirus olet.

m

Bock recognized the corolla, stamens and pistils as essential parts of many flowers, and was probably the first botanist of his day to feel the need for some kind of classification. He mistrusted superstitions and folklore until he had personally checked them, but in one matter he found that the gossip of old crones was right and Dioscorides wrong: ferns *did* produce seed at midnight on Midsummer's Eve. How he proceeded may be read in a sixteenth-century translation of his book:

> I have foure yeres together one after an other upon the vigill of saynt John the Baptiste (whiche we call in Englishe mydsomer even) soughte for this sede of Brakes upon the nyghte, and in dede I fownde it earlye in the mornynge before the daye brake, the sede was small blacke and lyke unto poppye. I gatherid it after this maner: I laide shetes and mollen leaves underneth the brakes whiche receyved the sede . . . I went aboute this busynes, all figures coniurynges, saunters, charmes, wytchcrafte, and sorseryes sett a syde, takynge wyth me two or three honest men to bere me companye.[1]

Bock *Kreütter Bůch* Pinks (*Dianthus* sp.), p. ccxviii.

1 Quoted by Arber (1986), p. 61.

How odd that it did not occur to Bock to see whether or not this happened at other times also!

In 1546 Bock, by judicious saving, was in a position to subsidize an illustrated edition of his herbal, now renamed *Kreuter Bůch*. His artist and engraver, David Kandel of Strasbourg, was young and self-taught, and many of his figures – some 550 in all – were taken from Fuchs and elsewhere. This is a pity, because his own designs are often both competent and original, especially several of trees which he has enlivened by the introduction of animals and human beings. We see, for example, Thisbe finding the dead body of Pyramus under a mulberry, peasants dancing to the tunes of the bagpipes beneath the shade of a lime, and the intoxicated Noah and his sons beneath a canopy of vines. In his preface, which is dedicated to 'Highborn Princes, and Lords, Lord Philip, Landgraf of Hessen, etc.', Bock urges his readers 'to avoid and flee from all vagabonds, gypsies, Jews and roguish knaves with their idle chatter, quack cures and deceitful vermifuges'.

Bock's book sold far better than Brunfels's, better even than those of Fuchs. At least a dozen further editions, with additional woodcuts, were called for, and a Latin translation appeared in 1552; but the 1546 edition remains the most attractive.

The Herbal in Italy, Portugal and Spain

Between the years 1530 and 1590, five great collections of wood-blocks were produced: those of Brunfels and of Fuchs which we have already mentioned; a Swiss–German group formed by Gesner and Camerarius; the great Plantin assemblage in Antwerp; and finally those that were made for Mattioli in Italy. Most of these were used time and again, legitimately or pirated, sometimes reduced or reversed in copying, over the next two centuries. In this chapter we shall chiefly consider the works of Mattioli, compiler of the most influential Italian herbal of the sixteenth century, and more briefly those of several other Italian, Spanish and Portuguese botanists of the period.

Pierandrea Mattioli, or Matthiolus (1501–77), the son of a

Sienese doctor who left his native town to practise in Venice, was intended for the law but chose to follow in his father's footsteps. After studying in Venice and Padua he set up a practice in Siena, then one in Rome, where he remained until the sack of the city by the armies of Charles V in 1527. For the next fourteen years we find him in Valle Anania, near Trent (Trento), then as town physician of Görz (Gorizia) for a further fourteen years. His popularity in Gorizia is evinced by the fact that when his house was burnt down his patients clubbed together to replace what he had lost, while the municipality advanced him a year's salary. In 1544, Valgrisi of Venice published, in Italian and without illustrations, the first edition of his famous commentaries on Dioscorides, *Commentarii in sex libros Pedacii Dioscoridis*. The first illustrated edition (1554), with 562 small woodcuts, was reprinted many times, in both Latin and Italian, and it is said that in all some thirty-two thousand copies were sold.

Mattioli's fame spread rapidly, and in 1555 he was summoned to Prague by the Emperor Ferdinand I to treat his son the Archduke Maximilian. Here he remained for more than twenty years in the imperial service, and here, too, was first published the vast folio edition of his *Commentarii*, with large woodcut illustrations and Czech text (Girkii Melantryka, 1562). Seven further editions followed between 1562 and 1604 with texts in German, Latin and Italian, and in all the *Commentarii* was issued, in various formats and five different languages, at least forty-five times. It is rather shaming that no Englishman ever ventured to undertake the formidable task of translating it.

Since some of our readers may have never handled a Mattioli folio – beside which the 1597 Gerard is a mere featherweight and even Fuchs no serious competitor in bulk – it may be of interest if we give some idea of its immensity. The preliminaries, including indexes, run to about 150 pages, most in double columns of tiny print. These are followed by Dioscorides' own brief foreword, on which Mattioli has written a commentary of some fourteen thousand words *in a single paragraph*! Indeed, throughout he has sometimes seen fit to make his comments up to twenty times the length of the text under discussion. Dioscorides' bestiary, with figures ranging from the elephant and hippopotamus to a double bed infested with bed-bugs, is of course also included. In short, only those accustomed to let their Great Dane sleep on their bed should contemplate choosing the Mattioli folio, or other such monsters as Johnson's Gerard or Parkinson's *Herball*, for a bedside book.

The artists who made both the small and the large woodcuts for the *Commentarii* were an Italian, Giorgio Liberale of Udine, and a German named Wolfgang Meyerpeck; how they divided their labours is not stated, but probably Liberale was the draughtsman. The big set of figures is in every way so immeasurably superior to the small that we shall limit our comments to the former. Spectacular though some of these undoubtedly are, and brilliant always the dexterity of the engraver (especially when dealing with such intricate subjects as the conifers), the fact remains that we find in Mattioli neither the marvellous observations and sensitivity of Weiditz nor the dignified if at times rather bleak simplicity of the artists who worked for Fuchs. Certainly no one could accuse Liberale and Meyerpeck of

Colour plates
Page 134 Brunfels *Herbarum Vivae Eicones* Waterlily (*Nymphaea alba*), vol. I, 36.
Page 135 Brunfels *Herbarum Vivae Eicones* Violets (*Viola canina* and V. odorata), vol. I, 137.

133

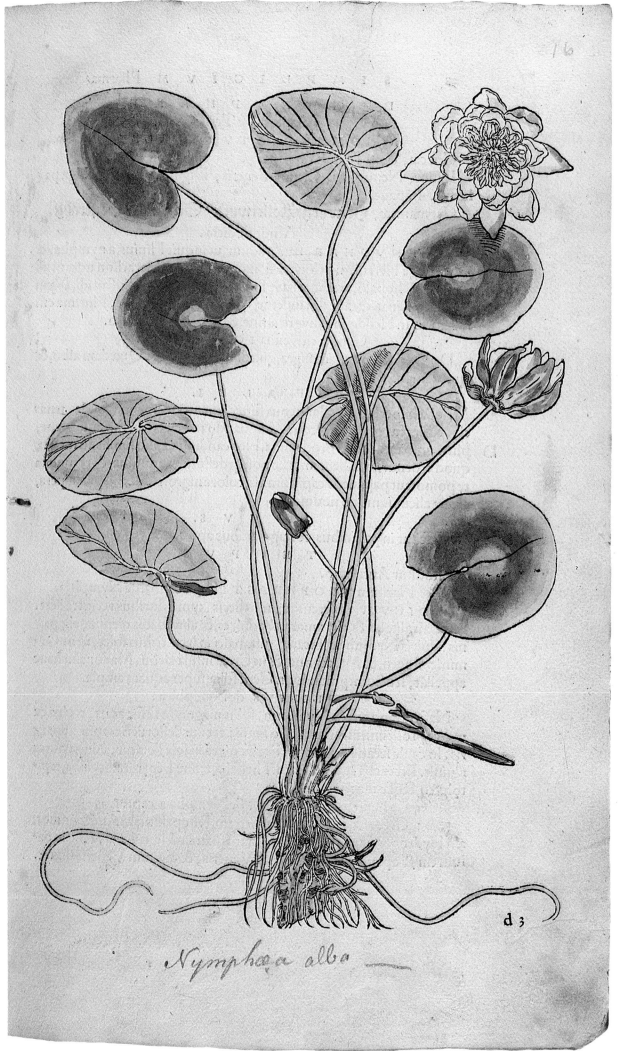

d 3

Nymphæa alba

134

Viola canina

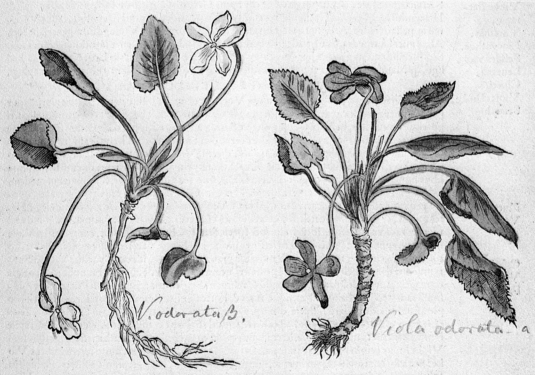

V. odorata β. *Viola odorata a*

DE VIOLIS RHAPSODIA XX.
Nomenclaturæ, Violæ Nigræ.

Græcæ, ἰόν μέλαν. λευπόδιον. ἰόν ἄγριον. τιριαπήϊον. κυβίλιον.

Latinæ, Seſſilis. Muraria Viola. Viola nigra. Viola purpurea.

Germanicæ, Blaw Violaten. Gel Violaten. Brun Violaten. Zam Violaten. Wild Violaten.

m 2

bleakness. Shading is so extensively employed that although early copies of Mattioli were sometimes coloured – Wotton expressly states that it was a *coloured* copy of the edition in Italian that he bequeathed in his will to Queen Henrietta Maria – the book is more effective in black and white. Exception must, however, be made of two copies printed on blue-grey paper and picked out in silver: one is in the Sächsische Landesbibliothek in Dresden; the other, only in part so treated, belonged at one time to Sydney Cockerell and is now in the Oak Spring Garden Library at Upperville, Virginia. The black-and-white photograph of spruce gives no idea of its beauty.

Mattioli's artists were also tiresomely conscious of the formal shape of the rectangular blocks. Where the subject is crowded, this frequently results – as on occasion with Fuchs – in producing the effect of a wallpaper or chintz. One has only to compare Mattioli's 'Carduus' (thistle, *Carduus* sp.) with Brunfels's pulsatilla or one of the less confined cuts in Fuchs such as that of maize to see what is gained by forgetting the rectangle. An extreme example of the Mattioli 'chintz', and one which also demonstrates the phenomenal skill and ingenuity of the cutter, is the 'Psyllium' (plantain, *Plantago psyllium*). Some of the blocks have survived in good condition, after being taken to France in the 1750s by H. L. Duhamel du Monceau. The last hundred or so, many still fit for printing, including that of the second image of a tulip seen in Europe, were sold in 1989[1].

Mattioli seems to have suffered in middle life what would today be called a 'personality change'. The man so adored by the townsfolk of Gorizia became in time besotted with Dioscorides. Confident that he and his hero alone could be right, he maliciously attacked any who dared to criticize; and being so influential in Prague he was able to ruin their careers. A Portuguese Jew, baptized under the name of Amatus Lusitanus (Mattioli made a point of calling him 'Amathus'),[2] was denounced to the Inquisition, robbed of all his possessions and forced to seek refuge in a Turkish ghetto. Luigi Anguillara, a very capable botanist who had travelled widely in the Levant in pursuit of Dioscoridean plants, was rash enough to challenge some of Mattioli's identifications, only to find himself dismissed from his professorship in Padua University. Even the great Gesner did not escape the maestro's venom.

Yet Mattioli was far from omniscient and his figures are not always reliable. Though Busbecq[3] brought him drawings of plants from Turkey in 1562 and had previously supplied him with both living and dried specimens, he seems to have kept no systematic herbarium. There are false identifications in the book, and errors due to the use made by his artists of dried plants reconstituted by soaking in water. We have nowhere seen it mentioned that the figure of the banana is really printed upside down, and repeated thus in Gerard in 1597.

Anderson refers to 'one other blemish on Mattioli's career' – the experiments the botanist made on condemned prisoners to see whether monkshood (*Aconitum napellus*) was the most poisonous member of the genus. The results apparently confirmed his suspicions that this was so.

In 1577, Mattioli retired to Trento, where within the year he had died of the plague. Probably not many tears were shed.

1 'The provenance of the Mattioli woodblocks is interesting. After having been used for a number of editions until the 17th century, they were then apparently lost track of until Duhamel du Monceau came upon them and used some of them again with excellent results for his *Traité des Arbres et Arbustes*, 1755. The rest remained in his château until 1956, when they were sold and dispersed . . .' (Hunt *Catalogue*, vol. I (1958), 98). See Raphael, *The Mattioli Woodblocks* (1989).
2 From *amathēs*, Greek for 'stupid', 'ignorant' or 'boorish'. See Anderson (1977), p.168, and Karl Jessen (1864, reprint 1948), p.174.

3 See p.16.

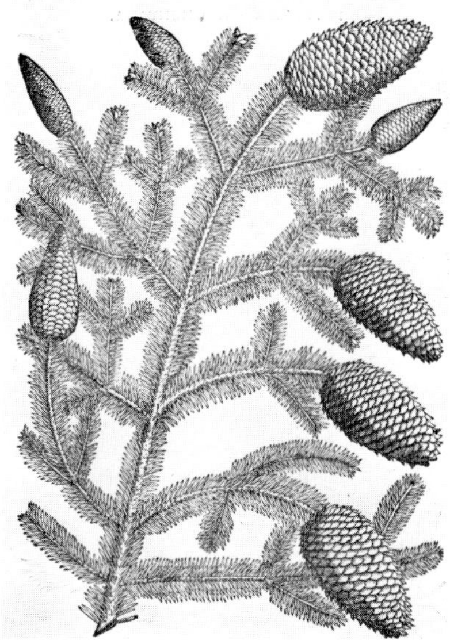
PICEA.

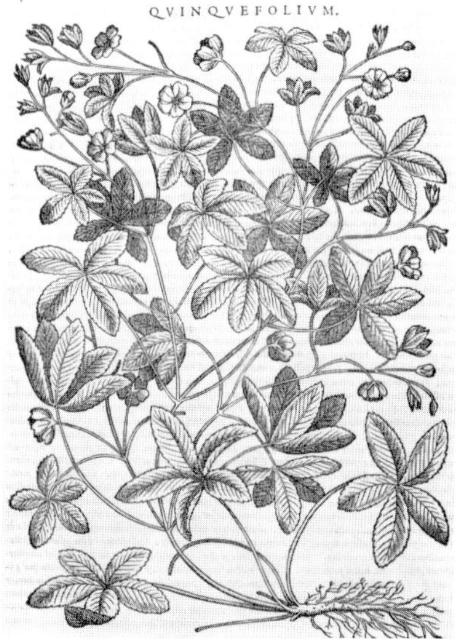
1018
And.Matthioli Comm.
QVINQVEFOLIVM.

Far left
Mattioli *Commentarii* Spruce (*Picea* sp.), p. 97.

Left
Mattioli *Commentarii* Cinquefoil (*Potentilla* sp.), p. 1018.

Σκόλιμος. CARDVVS. CAP. XIIII.

CArduus, Græci ſcolymon uocant †, folia chamæleonis habet, & albæ ſpinæ, nigriora, & craſſiora: caulem[a] longum edit, folioſum, capite ſpinoſo: radice[b] nigra, & craſſa. Quæ illita grauεolentiam alarum, totiusque corporis emendat: item ſi decocta in uino bibatur: copioſam autem urinam, fœtidamque expellit. Herba cùm recens tenereſcit, in olera, aſparagi modo, tranſit.

CARDVVS, SIVE CINARA ACVLEATA.

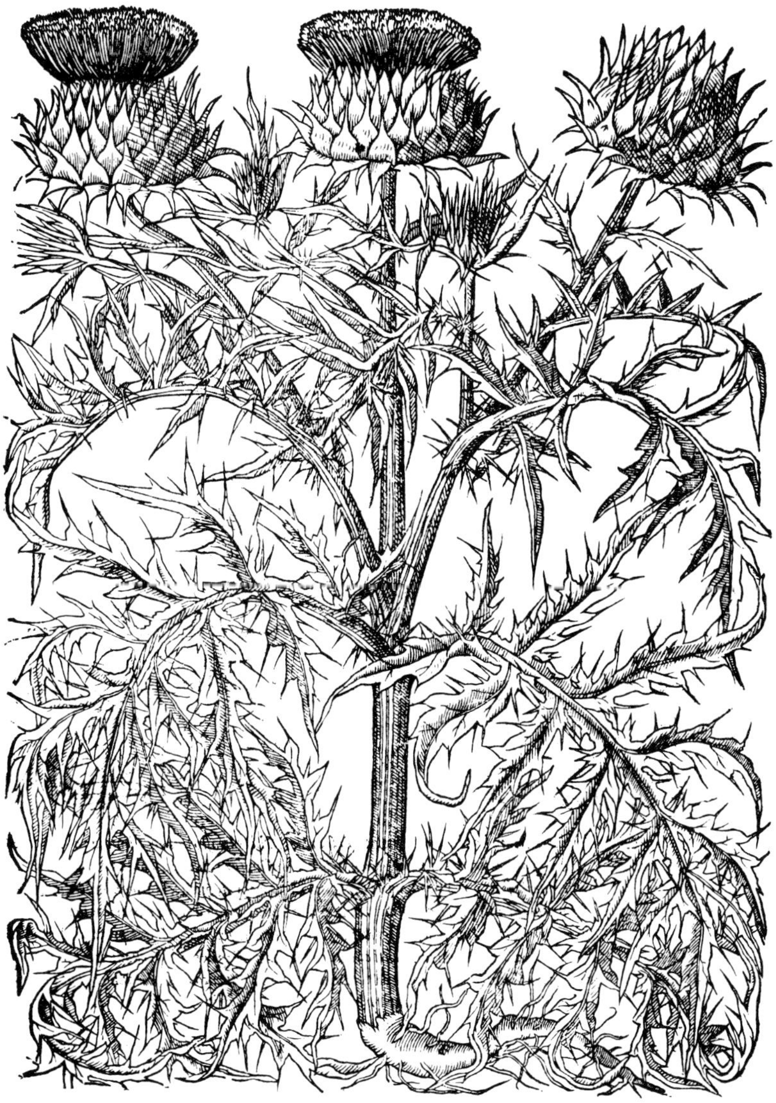

Mattioli *Commentarii* Thistle (*Carduus* sp.), p. 667.

Colour plates
Page 138 Meyer Greater celandine (*Chelidonium majus*).
Page 139 Meyer Asparagus (*Asparagus sylvestris*).

CHELIDONIVM MAIVS   Groß ſcholkraut.

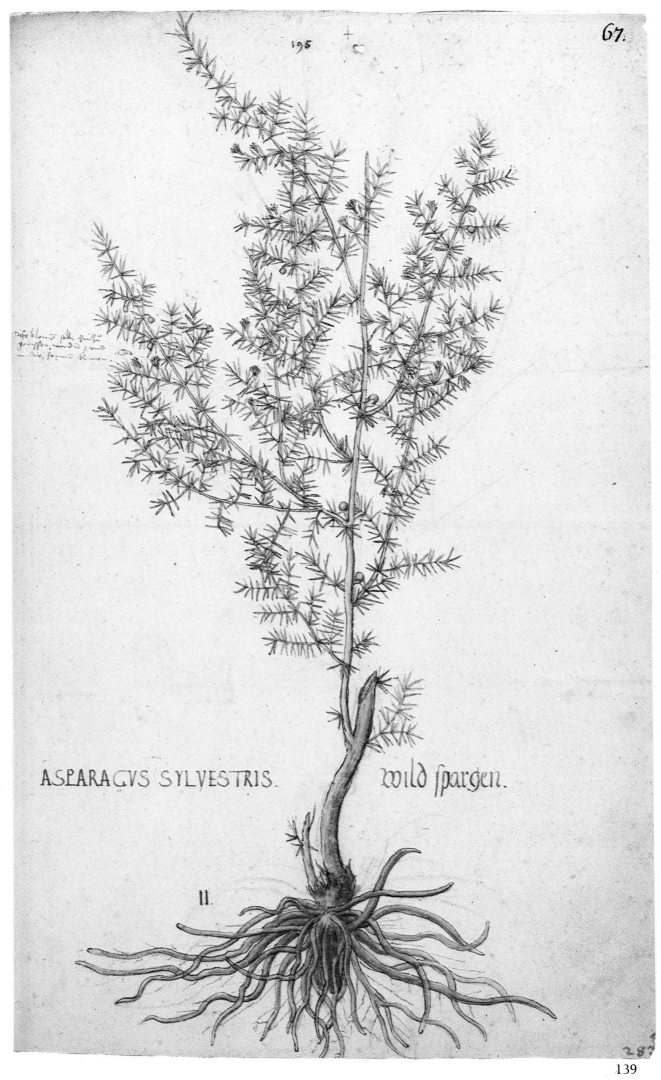

195

ASPARAGVS SYLVESTRIS.   wild ſpargen.

II.

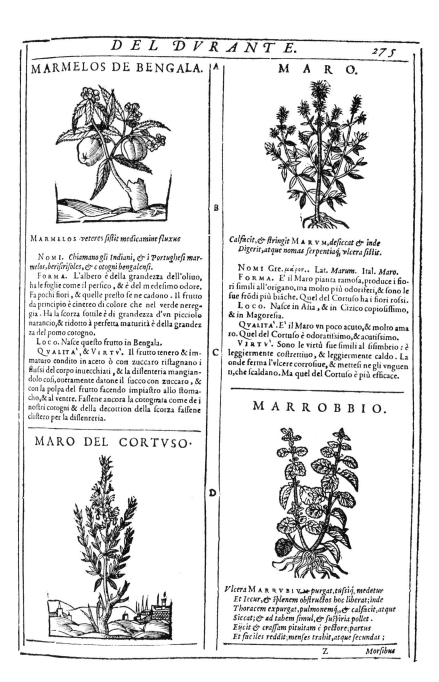

Durante *Herbario Nuovo* Quince (*Cydonia vulgaris*), thymes (*Thymus* sp.) and horehound (*Marrubium vulgare*), p. 275.

Three further Italians – Castore Durante, Giambattista della Porta and Prospero Alpini – should not be overlooked.

Castore Durante (1523–90) was born at Spoleto and studied at the Sapienza Archiginnasio (later university) in Rome. He published his *Herbario Nuovo* there in 1585, and was appointed physician to Sixtus V, who became pope in the same year; but both men had only five more years to live.

Durante was poet, doctor and botanist, and his herbal, which deals with the medicinal plants of Europe and of both the East and West Indies, gained its considerable popularity from its quaint charm rather than from its botanical value. Each of its chapters – and there are almost a thousand of them – is crowned with a little woodcut, barely 7.5 × 5 cm (3 × 2 in.), by a certain Isabella Parasole, who alternated theft from Fuchs and Mattioli with whimsicalities all her own. What Arber calls the *Herbario Nuovo*'s 'pleasingly unscientific' plant descriptions are in Latin verse. We reproduce from it the page showing a quince, two kinds of thyme and horehound.

Arber[1] translates in full the legend attached to a tree unknown to science – the 'Arbor Malenconico' or 'Arbor Tristis' – whose trunk had human shape. The tree is said to have sprung from the ashes of an Indian maiden who killed herself for love of the Sun when he did not return her affection. As an echo of her disappointment, the flowers of the tree 'shrink from the Sun, and never open in his presence', blooming at night and giving forth 'a delicious perfume'. Once the Sun rises, the tree looks faded, withered and dead.[2]

A German translation of the *Herbario Nuovo* was published in Frankfurt am Main in 1609, and Italian editions continued to be produced for more than a century after this.

Giambattista della Porta, who was born in Naples in about 1535 and lived until 1605, was part scientist, part dupe, and no doubt part charlatan also: a great traveller too, tireless in his pursuit of knowledge, but unable – or unwilling? – to differentiate between fact and fiction. In addition to his famous *Phytognomonica* (Naples, 1588) and various works on magic he also wrote innumerable comedies and several tracts on agriculture; but it is only his *Phytognomonica* ('Plant Indicators') that concerns us here.

Della Porta was an ardent advocate of a famous pseudo-scientific theory, the 'doctrine of signatures',[3] whose great champion was Theophrastus Bombast von Hohenheim (1493–1541), better known as Paracelsus; he also dabbled in astrological botany, derived from Aristotle and much propagated by Nicholas Culpeper in England in the seventeenth century.[4] The doctrine of signatures proclaimed that the Almighty, in His infinite wisdom and goodness, gave man a broad hint as to the use to which plants could be put. For example, those with heart-shaped fruit or bulbous roots were suitable for the treatment of cardiac troubles, those with yellow sap for sufferers from jaundice. Maidenhair fern helped the balding; herbs with articulated seed-pods counteracted the venom of scorpions, while scaly objects such as toothwort (*Dentaria* sp.), pomegranates, and pine-cones relieved toothache. That many of these alleged treatments proved perfectly useless, whereas other herbs apparently unsigned by the Creator were efficacious, failed to shake the faith of true believers in the doctrine. Such nonsense persists in certain quarters to this day.

Bartholomäus Carrichter's *Horn des Heyls Menschlicher Blödigkeit oder Kreütterbůch* (Strasbourg, 1576), described as 'a monument to human weaknesses and follies', and the scarcely less foolish *Historia sive Descriptio Plantarum* of Leonhardt Thurneisser zum Thurn (Berlin, 1578) are among other works directed at the credulous which, like the *Phytognomonica*, are illustrated with better woodcuts than they deserve.

With Prospero Alpini (1553–1617) – whose name is sometimes written Alpino – we return again to sanity.

In 1580 this able physician and botanist, who had studied at Padua University, accompanied the newly appointed Venetian consul to Egypt, where he spent three profitable years investigating the country's medicinal and economic plants. Alpini's *De Medicina Aegyptiorum* (1591) was followed a year

1 (1986), pp.102–3.

2 Compare the classical story of Clytie, Ovid, *Metamorphoses*, Book 4.

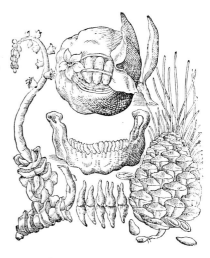

Porta *Phytognomonica Dentaria* sp., pomegranate (*Punica granatum*) and pine cone, 1591 edition, p.211.

3 See the chapter in Arber (1986), pp.247–63.
4 See p.182.

Colour plates
Page 142 Fuchs *De Historia Stirpium* Cherry, p.425.
Page 143 Fuchs *De Historia Stirpium* Rose, p.657.

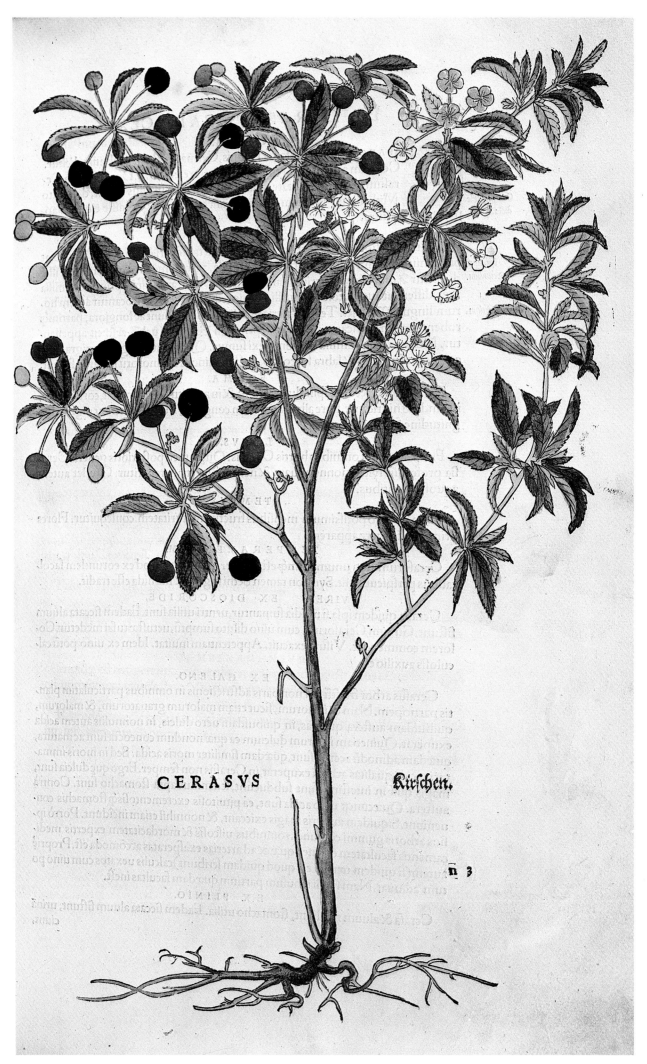

CERASVS   Kirſchen.

ñ 3

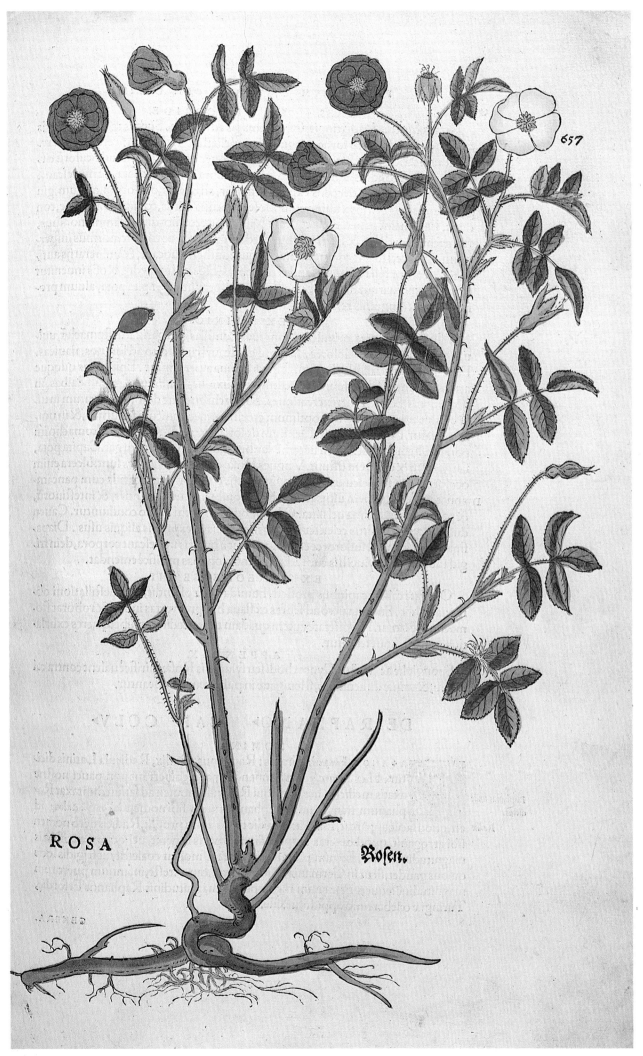

ROSA   Roſen.

657

143

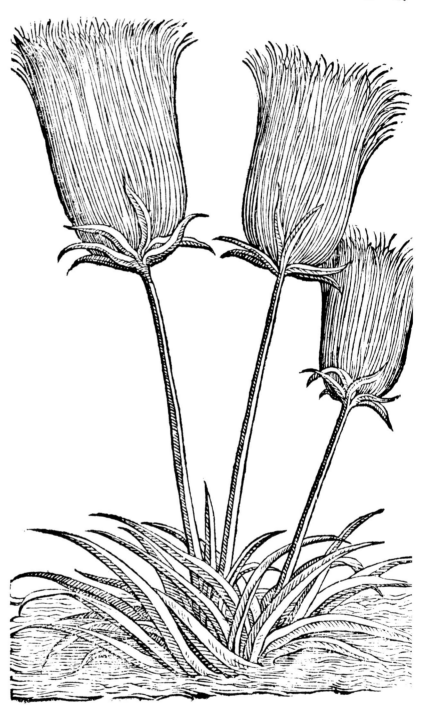

Alpini *De Plantis Aegypti* Papyrus
(*Cyperus papyrus*), p. 43.

later by his best-known work, *De Plantis Aegypti Liber*, both
published in Venice and illustrated with woodcuts. Those in the
former are gruesome and of medical interest only; but the latter
contains a number of good figures of the native flora, from which
we have selected that of the papyrus (*Cyperus papyrus*). Alpini is
believed to have been the first European to mention the coffee
plant, which he saw growing in Cairo. He eventually became
professor of botany at Padua, the oldest chair in that faculty in
Europe, and introduced many Egyptian plants into the botanic
gardens there.

For our early knowledge of the medicinal and economic herbs of the East and West Indies we are chiefly indebted to the Portuguese and the Spaniards respectively.

Garcia da Orta[1] was born some time during the last decade of the fifteenth century at Elvas, a little Portuguese fortified frontier town best remembered today for the delectable plums which it exports. After studying medicine at two Spanish universities, he returned to Portugal and practised as a village doctor until 1532 when he was appointed a lecturer at Lisbon University. But presumably he hankered after a more adventurous life, for two years later he seized an opportunity to sail to Goa, the Portuguese settlement on the western coast of India which had been established by Albuquerque some twenty years earlier.

Here was an exciting and entirely uninvestigated flora, and Orta soon realized that he had material to occupy him profitably for an indefinite period; in fact, he was to remain in Goa until his death thirty-six years later, and we are the beneficiaries of his long stay there. His particular concern was with plants potentially of use as drugs. Indefatigable in his search after knowledge, he questioned natives and travellers, and finally produced a scholarly pioneer work still of the greatest importance: *Coloquios dos Simples, e Drogas he Cousas Mediçinais da India*, first published in Goa in 1563 and now extremely rare. It was one of the earliest books to be printed in India.

The *Coloquios* is in the form of a dialogue between Orta and a certain Dr Ruano – 'a fictitious alter ego who represented theoretical knowledge as opposed to the pragmatism of da Orta'.[2] Now at a safe distance from Europe, Orta felt free to express unorthodox opinions; as he himself wrote, 'Even I, when in Spain, did not dare to say anything against Galen or against the Greeks.' Ginger, cinnamon, betel nut (*Piper betle*, here illustrated), cloves, nutmeg and mace are among the plants investigated; but, like all agreeable authors, Orta allowed himself to digress, informing us, for example, how to tame elephants, and listing the native names for the pieces on a chessboard.

Various editions of the *Coloquios* followed in several languages, Clusius producing in 1567 an abridgement, several times reprinted, in Latin,[3] which was retranslated into English (1577), Italian (1582) and French (1619). These versions were all very inadequate, and since the virtually unprocurable original continued to retain its value, a repeated call for its reissue was eventually answered. In 1897 the Conde de Ficalho produced and annotated what has become the standard edition, and an English translation of it and introduction by Sir Clements Markham was published in 1913.

The first edition of the *Coloquios* was unillustrated; but Clusius provided figures for his emasculated edition of 1567, and other translators followed suit. There was, however, another Portuguese doctor, Christoval Acosta (*c.* 1515–80),[4] who also visited Goa, where he became acquainted with Orta, and on his return to Europe published in Spanish a book, *Tractado de las Drogas y Medicinas de las Indias Orientales con sus Plantas* (Burgos, 1578), which owed much to the labours of his compatriot. Of particular interest is the fact that this work was illustrated with woodcuts which (says Jessen), though crude, were drawn from nature. They include various tropical spices

Orta *Aromatum* Betel (*Piper betle*), p. 95.

1 It is sometimes difficult to track him down in indexes, since he is also to be found under Dorta, Da Horta, Huerto, Del Huerto, Garzia, etc.

2 Anderson (1977), p.204.

3 Clusius's copy of the *Coloquios*, annotated in Latin in a microscopic but perfectly legible italic hand, is said by Arber to be still extant. There is also a copy of Clusius's translation of Orta's *Aromatum . . . Historia* (1567) in the Bodleian Library (pressmark Sherard 42). It is annotated in two hands, one of which appears to be that of Clusius.
4 Arber (1938) describes him as a Spaniard.

Colour plates
Page 146 Dodoens *Crŭÿdeboeck*, title-page, signed by the artist H(ans) L(iefrinck).
Page 147 Potato (*Solanum tuberosum*). A drawing from the Plantin collection, which may have been used by Clusius.

APOLLO.

ÆSCVLAPIVS.

GENTIVS

ARTHEMISIA

METHRI
DATES

ILYSIMACHVS

Cruijdeboeck.

In den welcken die ghehee
le historie/dat es Tgheslacht/tfatsoen/naem/na-
tuere/cracht ende werckinghe/ van den Cruyden/
niet alleen hier te lande waffende / maer oock van
den anderen vremden in der Medecijnen oorboor-
lijck/met grooter neerstichept begrepen ende
verclaert es/met der feluer Cruyden na
tuerlick naer dat leuen conterfeytfel
daer by gheftelt.

DEr hoochgheborene ende alder doorluchtich-
fte Coninghinne ende Vrouwe/Vrouw Ma-
rien Coninghinne Douaigiere van Hungheren/
ende Bohemen rc. Regente ende Gouuernante
van des K. M. Neerlanden/toeghefcreuen.

Duer D. Rembert Dodoens/Medecijn van
der ftadt van Mechelen.

P HESPERIDVM HORTI B

Taratoufli· à Philipp de Sivry
acceptum Viennæ 26 Ianuarij
1588.
Papas Peruanum Petri Ciecæ.

147

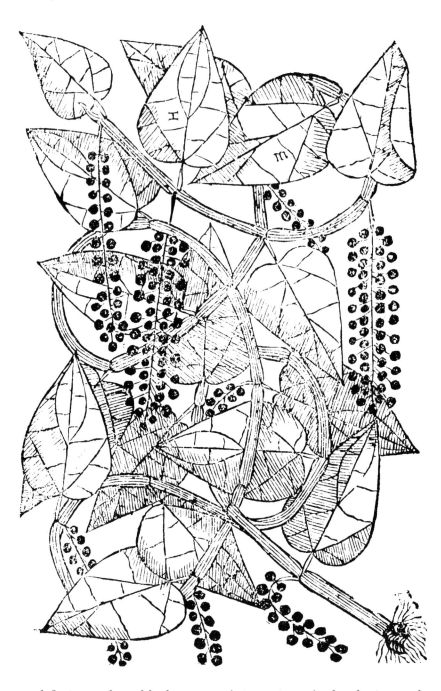

Acosta *Tractado* Pepper (*Pimenta nigra*), p. 19.

1 The industrious Clusius also published, in 1582, an abridged Latin translation of the *Tractado*.

and fruits such as black pepper (*Piper nigrum*), the durian and pineapple, and, incidentally, a splendid pair of elephants.[1]

Nicolás Monardes was born in Seville, probably in 1493 though various authorities suggest dates as late as *c*. 1512. After studying at Alcalá – for there was as yet no medical school at Seville University – he established himself as a fashionable physician in his native city, where he remained until his death in 1588. He never set foot in the New World, about whose medicinal plants and other related matters he wrote a best-seller from the material brought back to Spain by more adventurous men. His *Dos Libros . . .* appeared in two parts in 1569 and 1571, then in 1574 in a single volume. In that same year the Plantin press in Antwerp produced a condensed version done into Latin by Clusius, and in 1577 came an English translation by 'Jhon Frampton, Marchaunt', charmingly entitled *Joyfull Newes out of the Newe Founde Worlde*.

It must be admitted that Monardes swallowed a fair number of

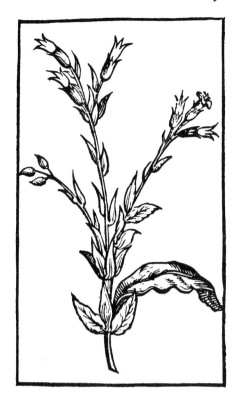

EL TABACO. 3

Nicotiana inserta infundibulo ex quo hauriunt fumũ Indi & nau cleri.

travellers' tales, and his book has been generously described as 'something less than a model of accuracy'. Nonetheless, it had considerable value at the time, and in its English version (reprinted in 1925 in the Tudor Translation series) still affords delightful reading to lovers of Elizabethan prose. Among the few illustrations is what is probably the first figure in a printed book of the tobacco plant (*Nicotiana tabacum*). It is not very good, and Clusius, in his Latin edition, wisely used a better and perhaps marginally later one from the Plantin collection. He also gives illustrations which include capsicums and sarsaparilla, and a delightful armadillo.

Here, to give a taste of the flavour of the *Joyfull Newes*, is a brief extract from Monardes's substantial account 'Of the Tabaco, and of his Greate Vertues'. Speaking of slaves, he observes that Negroes and Indians, when worn out by dancing, take tobacco 'at the nose and mouths', and after 'lying as though thei were dedde three or fower howers',

> thei doe remaine lightened, without any wearinesse, for to, laboure againe: and thei dooe this with so great pleasure, that although thei bee not wearie, yet thei are very desirous for to dooe it: and the thyng is come to so muche effecte, that their maisters doeth chasten theim for it, and doe burne the Tabaco, because thei should not use it, whereupon thei goe to the desartes, and secrete places to dooe it, because thei maie not bee permitted to drinke them selves drunke with wine, and therefore thei are gladde to make themselves drunken with the smoke of Tabaco.

Another Spaniard who wrote about the natural history and medical botany of the New World, and this time from personal experience, was Francisco Hernandez (*c.* 1514–87), physician to

Above left
Monardes *Dos Libros . . . Segunda Parte* Tobacco (*Nicotiana tabacum*), p. 3. Compare this straggly plant with the more accurate representation (above right) in l'Obel *Stirpium Adversaria Nova* Tobacco, p. 252.

Colour plates
Page 150 Gerard *Herball*, portrait of John Gerard. The contemporary colouring in this and the other pages reproduced from Bodley's copy of the first edition of Gerard is miraculously well preserved. The whole volume is in almost mint condition.
Page 151 Gerard *Herball*, title-page, 1597.

EFFIGIES IOANNIS GERAR= DI MESHYRII CIVIS ET CHIRVR= GI LONDINENSIS ANNO ÆTATIS SVÆ 53 1598

D. absent, buone.

De Præscientia Dei.

WP

150

THE
HERBALL
OR GENERALL
Hiſtorie of
Plantes.

Gathered by John Gerarde
of London Master in
CHIRVRGERIE.

Imprinted at London by
Iohn Norton.
1597

Hernandez *Plantarum . . . Historia*
Dahlia, p. 372.

Philip II. His expedition to Mexico, where he remained from 1571 to 1577, had royal backing on a lavish scale, and Hernandez was appointed 'Protomedico' – 'First Physician' – of the Indies.

On his return, the fruits of his immense labours – a bulky manuscript with innumerable drawings entitled *Rerum Medicarum Novae Hispaniae Thesaurus*, or 'Treasury of the Medicinal Things of New Spain' – was gratefully received by His Majesty, who had it all sumptuously bound in sixteen folio volumes, six of text and ten of illustrations, but did nothing to assist its publication. So Hernandez died without seeing a single word of his great *Thesaurus* in print. But worse was to follow: in 1671 a fire in the library of the Escorial destroyed all but a few fragments of the sixteen volumes, and one or more duplicate manuscripts of the text, which Hernandez was said to have left behind in Mexico as a precaution, had apparently vanished without trace.

Much, but happily not all, seemed to have been irrevocably lost. After Hernandez's death the King, perhaps ashamed at last of his treatment of the Protomedico of the Indies, ordered extracts of the *Thesaurus* to be prepared for publication. The first edition of this was eventually issued in Mexico in 1615, long after Philip's death, and a second in Rome in 1628; but the only fully illustrated edition was that produced in Rome in 1651. Among its figures is a good representation of the dahlia, or 'Cocoxochitl' as Hernandez called it – a plant long cultivated in Mexico in single and double forms of various colours, but which for some inexplicable reason was not successfully introduced into England until the beginning of the nineteenth century.

Another equally tardy arrival here, also first drawn and described by Hernandez, was the tigridia (*Tigridia pavonia*); the reasonably accurate woodcut of it, used as early as 1576 by l'Obel in his *Plantarum seu Stirpium Historia*, must have been derived from information sent to Spain by Hernandez before his return. Gerard, who oscillated between absurd credulity (the notorious goose-bearing barnacle tree) and no less unwarranted disbelief, reproduces this figure in his *Herball* (1597), but only to dismiss it as 'meere fiction'. The *Botanical Magazine* (1801, plate 533) states that the tigridia 'grew wild about Mexico, and was much cultivated for its excessive beauty and for the medicinal virtues of its root; being as [Hernandez] terms it, "a frigefacient in fevers, and also a promoter of fecundity in women".'

Linnaeus, naming a genus after the Spaniard, wrote in his *Critica Botanica*, 'Hernandia is an American tree, with the handsomest leaves of any, and less conspicuous flowers – from a botanist who had supreme good fortune, and who was highly paid to investigate the natural history of America; would that the fruits of his labours had corresponded to the expenditure!' However, twenty years ago there came exciting and unexpected news: 'A copy of Hernandez' enormous MS. volumes containing the results of his seven years' study of the natural history of Mexico has actually been discovered in Spain and awaits the detailed study that it has been denied for almost four hundred years.'[1] Perhaps this arduous task is already in hand: but there are no duplicates of the many hundreds of drawings; and except for those relatively few that were engraved, these have undoubtedly vanished for ever.

1 John Farquhar Fulton, 'Medical Aspects of Early Botanical Books', Hunt *Catalogue*, introductory essay, vol. I (1958), xxxiv.

The Herbal in the Low Countries, Switzerland and France

In Antwerp there still stands, little changed with the passing of the years, the handsome and ornate house, built round three sides of a rectangular courtyard, in which Christophe Plantin established in 1576 his world-famous printing works. The firm functioned continuously under the direction of the same family for three centuries, and the building is now the state-owned Musée Plantin-Moretus – Jean Moretus being the chief assistant, son-in-law and successor of Christophe Plantin.

Though I have not been back to the museum since 1926, I vividly recall how the whole world of sixteenth-century printing suddenly came alive to me as I saw the old presses, the proof-sheets still lying on the desks in the proof-readers' room, the cases filled with type and the furnaces for casting it, the cut and uncut wood-blocks, the old account books, and all the paraphernalia of the printer-publisher's trade. Everything has been preserved, and presumably the visitor can still buy, as I did, a copy printed from the original type and on one of the original presses of Plantin's charming autobiographical sonnet, 'Le Bonheur de ce Monde', beginning, 'Avoire une maison commode, propre & belle'.[1] He had – and it was here that were printed most of the works of the three great Flemish botanists of his day: Dodoens, Clusius and l'Obel.

These three men, though they went their separate ways, seem to have collaborated in complete harmony, selecting the figures that illustrate their works from what was virtually a common pool of wood-blocks under Plantin's charge, made after the literally thousands of drawings produced for Plantin by an artist named Pierre van der Borcht and his team. It will be convenient if we precede a discussion of the drawings and the woodcuts by some account of the careers of Plantin and his herbal authors, and the works they collaborated to produce.

Christophe Plantin (1514–88), a native of Touraine, studied bookbinding in Caen until, probably about 1550, he moved with his wife to Antwerp, where he set up shop as a binder and leather-worker. One night he was attacked in the street by a bunch of drunken revellers, one of whom, mistaking him for another man against whom he bore a grudge, ran him through with a sword. This happy accident – if one may so describe it – forced him to abandon relatively heavy work and turn to printing, a field in which he had already had some experience.

His success was immediate. He had a good deal of free labour to hand, for each of his many daughters, as soon as she reached the age of five, was put to proof-reading (and one of them went blind as a result). He had great business acumen. He was industrious, enterprising, and one might conjecture, ruthless. And he gave the world one of the greatest publishing houses of the sixteenth century.

Rembert Dodoens (Dodonaeus), the eldest of our three botanists, was born to patrician parents in Malines in 1517. After studying medicine at Louvain, he travelled widely and profitably through France, Italy and Germany, visiting many of their principal universities. In 1548 he was appointed town physician at Malines, and not long afterwards produced his first herbal,

1 Avoire une maison commode,
   propre & belle,
Un jardin tapissé d'espaliers
   odorans,
Des fruits, d'excellent vin, peu de
   train, peu d'enfans,
Posseder seul, sans bruit, une
   femme fidèle.

N'avoir dettes, amour, ni procés,
   ni querelle,
Ni de partage à faire avecque ses
   parens,
Se contenter de peu, n'espérer rien
   des Grands,
Régler tous ses desseins sur un
   juste modéle.

Vivre avec franchise & sans
   ambition,
S'adonner sans scrupule à la
   dévotion,
Domter ses passions, les rendre
   obéissantes.

Conserver l'esprit libre, & le
   jugement fort,
Dire son Chapelet en cultivant les
   entes,
C'est attendre chez soi bien
   doucement la mort.

Colour plates
Page 154 Gerard *Herball* Maize or sweet corn (*Zea mays*), p. 76.

Page 155 Gerard *Herball* Marigolds (*Calendula officinalis*), p. 600.

5 *Frumentum Indicum luteum.*
Yellow Turkie Wheate.

6 *Frumentum Indicum aureum.*
Gold coloured Turkie Wheate.

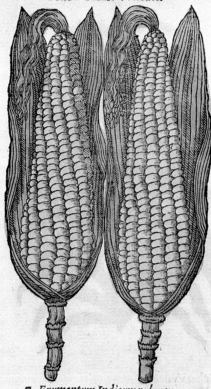

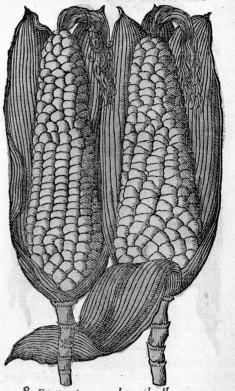

7 *Frumentum Indicum rubrum.*
Red Turkie Wheate.

8 *Frumentum cæruleum & album.*
Blew and white Turkie Wheate mixed

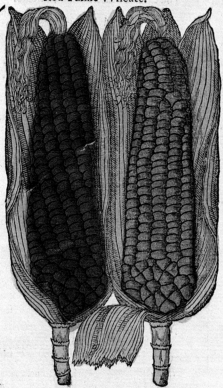

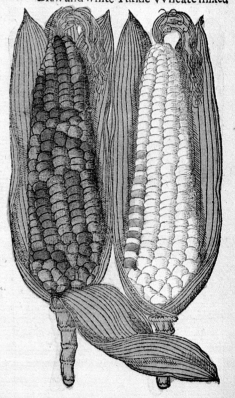

1 *Calendula multiflora maxima.*
The greatest double Marigold.

2 *Calendula maior polyanthos.*
The greater double Marigold.

3 *Calendula minor polyanthos.*
The smaller double Marigold.

4 *Calendula multiflora orbiculata.*
Double Globe Marigolde.

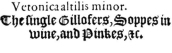

Vetonica altilis.
Carnations, and the double-cloaue Gillofers.

Vetonica altilis minor.
The single Gillofers, Soppes in wine, and Pinkes, &c.

Dodoens/Lyte *Nievve Herball* Pinks (*Dianthus* sp.), p. 154.

1 See colour plate p.146.

Crüÿdeboeck (1554), which owed much to Fuchs.[1] It was published in Antwerp by Jan van der Loe, the Plantin press being not as yet established. Almost immediately followed a French translation by Clusius, and it was mainly from this version that an amateur English botanist named Henry Lyte (*c.* 1529–1607) produced *A Nievve Herball* (1578), published in London but printed in Antwerp; the actual copy of the Clusius translation used by Lyte and copiously annotated by him is now in the British Library (pressmark 442. n.9).

In 1572 Dodoens received a double blow. First came the death of his wife. To mark the affection in which she was held, he rather touchingly made, at her funeral and in her name, a free distribution of strawberries and wine to the many mourners present. Then, a few months later, Malines was sacked by the Spaniards and everything he possessed was lost. From 1574 to 1578 Dodoens followed in Mattioli's footsteps as personal physician in Vienna to Maximilian II, and subsequently to his successor, Rudolf II. In 1582 he accepted the chair of medicine at Leiden, where he remained until his death three years later. Meanwhile there came from the Plantin press Dodoens's *magnum opus*: his *Stirpium Historiae Pemptades Sex* (1583) – a large folio of nearly nine hundred pages, illustrated with more than thirteen hundred woodcuts. *Pemptades* means 'lectures' or 'discourses'.

Charles de l'Écluse (1526–1609), better known as Carolus Clusius, was a native of Arras, at that time Flemish territory. After studying at various universities, he finally went to Montpellier to sit at the feet of Guillaume Rondelet, perhaps the greatest teacher of his day in the fields of medicine and natural history.

Clusius's life was not an easy one. His family, being Lutherans, suffered religious persecution which led to the confiscation of their property, and Charles reduced himself to penury to redeem it. He was also dogged by ill-health, suffering from 'an extraordinary proneness to fracture and dislocation of the limbs'. Yet he seemed to thrive on adversity, lived well into his eighties, and achieved, according to Arber, in addition to his professional skills 'an intimate acquaintance with Greek, Latin, Italian, Spanish, Portuguese, French, Flemish, German, law, philosophy, history, cartography, zoology, mineralogy, numismatics, and epigraphy'. He also wrote an exquisite italic hand.

His first original work, published by Plantin in 1576, was his *Rariorum aliquot Stirpium per Hispanias observatarum Historia*, the outcome of an expedition made with two friends to Spain and Portugal. In 1573 he was summoned by Maximilian II to Vienna, where he remained for about fourteen years, assisting with the imperial gardens and gleaning material for his book on the flora of 'Pannonia, Austria and thereabouts' which was issued, again by Plantin, in 1583. Soon he was everywhere recognized as the leading botanist in Europe, and with the co-operation of Busbecq and others was responsible for the introduction into Western Europe of the tulip, lilac, philadelphus, common laurel and horse-chestnut. Through him the potato – received from Philippe de Sivry, 'Lord of Waldheim and Governor of the town of Mons' – was disseminated throughout the Low Countries.[1]

He visited England more than once, meeting Sir Philip Sidney and obtaining through the good offices of Sir Francis Drake many plants from the New World. In 1601 the Plantin press published his collected works, *Rariorum Plantarum Historia*, which he had put together in Leiden where he spent the closing years of his long life. His death in 1609 was fittingly commemorated by the following epitaph:

When Clusius knew each plant Earth's bosom yields,
He went a-simpling in the Elysian fields.

Lastly comes Matthias de l'Obel (de Lobel, Lobelius). Born in Lille in 1538, he went, like Clusius and so many other talented young botanists of the day, to study under Rondelet at Montpellier. Rondelet, now nearly sixty, seems to have fallen under the spell of l'Obel's brilliance or charm, for on his death fourteen months later he left to his favourite pupil all his manuscripts.

This was in May 1566, and three years later l'Obel, together with a fellow student at Montpellier named Pierre Pena with whom he had been working, came to London, where they published jointly their *Stirpium Adversaria Nova* (Thomas Purfoot, 1570–71).[2] The book, the Latin of whose text is said to shock the purists, was dedicated to Queen Elizabeth, though how this honour came to be accorded to two young foreigners so recently arrived in England remains a mystery. How, too, did it happen that l'Obel was almost immediately put in charge of Lord Zouche's physic garden at Hackney? One can only postulate a fortunate combination of talent and charisma.

Pena, whose name precedes that of l'Obel on the title-page but whose precise contribution to this joint venture has never been established, remains a somewhat misty figure. In any case he now returned to France, where he became a successful doctor, and so passes out of our story. But l'Obel went from strength to strength.

[1] See colour plate p.147. For the tangled story of the introduction of the potato into Europe, see R. N. Salaman, *The History and Social Influence of the Potato* (London, 1949).

[2] See illustration p.149.

Colour plates
Page 158 Bulliard *Herbier de la France, Veratrum album*, vol. II, plate 155.
Page 159 Bulliard *Herbier de la France* Cornflower (*Centaurea cyanus*), vol. III, plate 221.

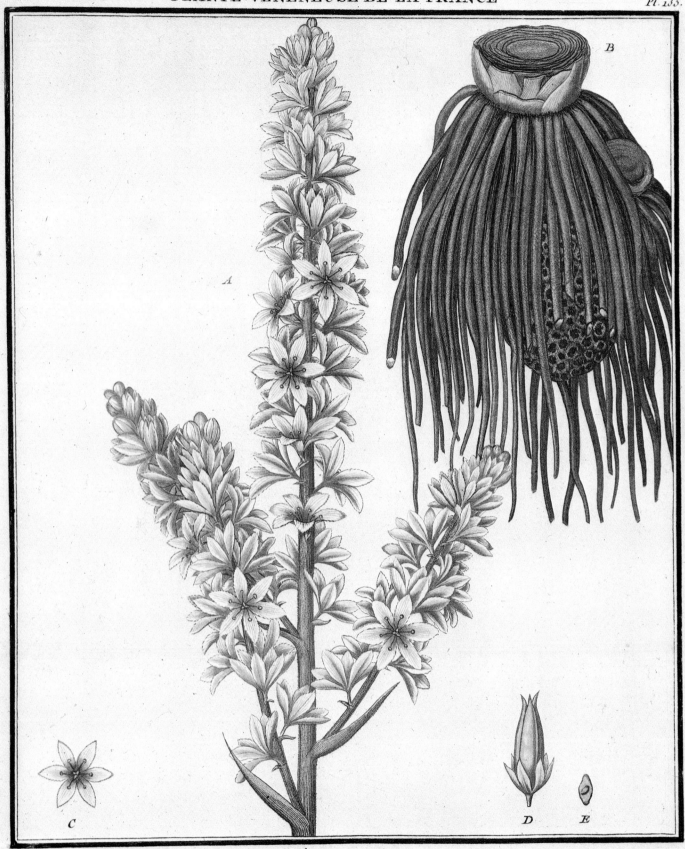

LE VERÂTRE BLANC. FL. FR.

Veratrum album. L. S. P. Polygam. monœc. 1479. Cette Plante est commune dans les Paturages de la Provence elle fleurit en Juillet et Aoust. sa tige haute de trois à quatre pieds est branchue, velue dans le haut et a un port qui diffère peu de celui du Verâtre noir; ses feuilles
sont aussi à peu pres de même. ses fleurs sont droites, portées sur des Pédoncules courts et composées chacune de six Pétales legerement dentés et
velues, de six étamines plus courtes que les Pétales, et de trois ovaires dont les Stygmates sont courts et divergents. chaque fleur a pour fruit trois capsu-
les univalves.

N° B. On voit fig. A l'extremité superieure de la tige de cette Plante de grandeur naturelle. on voit fig. B. sa racine telle qu'elle se trouve dans les Boutiques... fig. C.
une fleur separée. fig. D. ses fruits... fig. E. sa graine. Voyez aussi le N° B du Verâtre noir.
Cette espece de Veratrum est l'HELLEBORE BLANC des Boutiques, sa racine est émétique et fait éternuer avec violence.

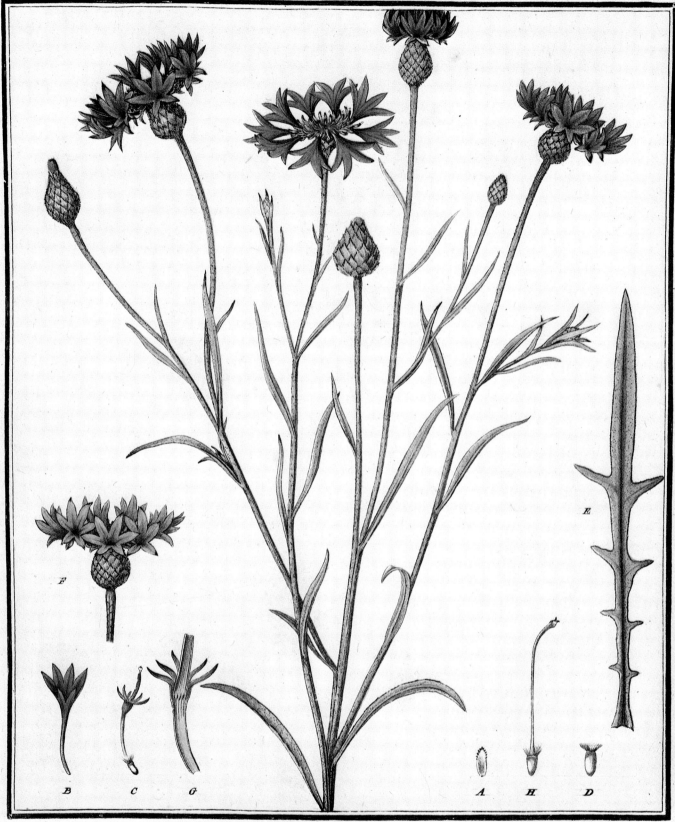

LA CENTAUREE BLUETTE... LE BLUET,

Centaurea cyanus. *L. S. P. syng. polygam. frustr. 1289...Cette plante est commune dans les champs; elle fleurit en juin et juillet;* *elle est annuelle... d'une racine fibreuse et solide s'elevent à la hauteur de deux pieds ou environ une tige cannelée et cotonneuse portant* *aux extremités de ses rameaux alternes une belle fleur flosculeuse composée d'un calice embriqué dont les ecailles A. sont dentées* *en leur bord, de fleurons steriles B. qui occupent la circonference de la fleur et de fleurons hermaphrodites C. qui en occupent le* *centre... un receptacle chargé de poils porte une vingtaine de semences couronnées d'une aigrette simple D... ses feuilles caulinai-* *res sont simples, les radicales E. sont pinnatifides.*

    N B. Il y a plusieurs belles varietés de cette plante la fig. F. represente celle à fleurs rouges... on voit fig. G. la coupe verticale d'un *fleuron hermaphrodite dessiné à la loupe... la fig. H. represente le pistil reposant encore sur son germe, ce pistil excede un peu la longueur* *des étamines qui sont au nombre de cinq et reunies en une colonne qui depasse de beaucoup le tube de chaque fleur,*

On a beaucoup venté autresfois les proprietés de cette plante en medecine; mais aujourd'huy il arrive rarement qu'on en fasse usage.

159

Plantin bought sheets from Purfoot of the *Stirpium Adversaria Nova*, enlarged it and republished it – rather confusingly – with the title *Nova Stirpium Adversaria* (1576). There followed from his press in 1581 a picture-book, *Plantarum seu Stirpium Icones*, consisting of more than two thousand of the woodcuts that constituted the Plantin 'pool', arranged and edited by l'Obel according to his new system of classification based on the character of a plant's leaves. That same year l'Obel became personal physician to William the Silent, and after the assassination three years later of the great Dutch liberator lived for a while in Antwerp. The last years of his life were spent in England, where in 1607 he was appointed 'Botanicus Regius' – 'Botanist Laureate' as it were – to King James I. He died at Highgate in 1616.

It is amusing, as Arber points out, to note that the frontispiece of one of l'Obel's books 'bears a device of white poplars as "armes parlantes", his name having taken its origin, traditionally, from the abele tree. The *Lobelia*, which was dedicated to him, thus has a name with an odd history, since it has migrated from a plant to a man, and then to another plant.' Similarly, Linnaeus, who took his name from a famous lime tree (Swedish *lind*) on a family estate, with mock modesty asked that it should be handed on to the *Linnaea borealis* – a plant 'lowly, insignificant, flowering but for a brief space – from Linnaeus who resembles it'. One could have wished that l'Obel had not been commemorated by a genus which, though it includes many noble species, is usually associated with the horrors of Victorian bedding.

It was probably under the direction of Clusius that Plantin's team of artists worked to produce the most extensive corpus of botanical illustrations assembled in the sixteenth century.[1] Of the 2117 drawings formerly in the Preussische Staatsbibliothek in Berlin (pressmark Libri picturati A16-31) no less than 1856 are of plants; most of these appear to have been executed between 1566 and 1573, and the principal botanical artist, of whom we know sadly little, was a certain Pierre van der Borcht (1545–1608), who was paid twelve or thirteen sous a drawing. He fled from his native Malines when it was sacked by the Duke of Alba in October 1572, and was given full-time employment, principally as a metal-engraver, by Plantin, for whom he had previously been working freelance.

When drawings could be made from living specimens, they were finished in full colour; but if these were not available, the artists, to avoid error, preferred to work in black and white only. Plants from all parts of Europe are represented, together with a number from India, America and elsewhere, particular attention being given to those of medicinal interest.

Now that the originals are once more accessible in Krakow, it is possible to form some idea of van der Borcht's stature as a botanical artist, as well as the extent of his contribution to the Plantin collection, both the drawings and the blocks made from them, many of which are still in the Plantin-Moretus Museum in Antwerp. From this evidence the fine quality of the drawings is clear. Whether his models were living or dried plants, it is clear that van der Borcht was an extremely good botanical draughtsman, and that he and his fellow block-cutters did an adequate

1 During the Second World War the collection was removed to the Benedictine Abbey at Grüsau, in Silesia, and taken thence to Poland. They are now in the Jagiellonian Library at Krakow.

Part of the important collection of musical manuscripts also sent to Grüsau, including holographs by Bach, Mozart, and Beethoven, has been returned to the Deutsche Staatsbibliothek in East Berlin. (See P. J. Whitehead's report on the Grüsau manuscripts in the *Times Literary Supplement*, 26 May 1978, p.594.)

job. The importance of the collection lies largely in its size, and in the abundant use that was made of the blocks, and copies of them, for many years to come.

One drawing that has been photographed is an especially interesting one. It shows the dragon tree, *Dracaena draco*, a native of the Canary Islands, which had been introduced in the previous century into the Iberian peninsula. This remarkable tree is to be found in engravings by Martin Schongauer (d. 1491) and other German and Flemish fifteenth-century artists, but the specimen here portrayed was seen by Clusius in a monastery garden in Lisbon. We can at least compare it with the woodcuts that were made from it, the first of which appeared, reversed, in Clusius's *Rariorum . . . per Hispanias* in 1576; one may also be seen, crudely re-cut and once more reversed, on page 1339 of Gerard's *Herball* (1597), and another on page 1523 of the 1633 and 1636 editions of Gerard, where it is printed from the block used by Clusius.[1] Once again, 'adequate' is the word that comes to mind. These woodcuts serve their purpose; but they lack all the refinement of the original, and if van der Borcht was the cutter (which is also by no means certain) he was either not outstandingly gifted in this craft or – and perhaps more likely – pushed by an importunate publisher.

The woodcuts of the Plantin pool, set beside those in Brunfels, Fuchs, or the big Mattioli, immediately make it evident that a steady decline has set in – a decline that was not to be arrested. With the introduction, towards the close of the sixteenth century, of metal-engraving in the service of botanical illustration, and with the gradual retreat of the herbal before the growing popularity of the florilegium, the great days of the herbal begin to draw to a close.

The Swiss naturalist Konrad Gesner[2] (1516–65), known as 'the Pliny of his age', was sent in 1533 by the city fathers of Zürich to Paris to broaden his mind. His immortal *Historia Animalium* was intended to have been followed by an equally splendid *Historia Plantarum*, for which he accumulated some fifteen hundred drawings, the majority of them original, and some wood-blocks made from them. On his death his material was left to his friend Kaspar Wolf, who found the task of dealing with it beyond his powers. After contributing a few of the woodcuts to form an appendix to Simler's *Vita Conradi Gesneri* (1566) he therefore sold his Gesneriana to the Nuremberg botanist Joachim Camerarius the Younger (1534–98), who incorporated a part of them in his own publications. Finally, in the eighteenth century, Gesner's drawings and blocks were acquired by Dr Trew, city physician of Nuremberg, who handed them over with other Gesner material to Casimir Schmiedel, professor of botany at the University of Erlangen. In 1753 and 1771 Schmiedel published about one third of all this in two fine folio volumes with hand-coloured illustrations.

The collection then vanished without trace until it was rediscovered in 1929 by a Swiss historian of science, Bernhard Milt, in an attic of Erlangen Univerity. Fine facsimilies of the watercolours were printed in eight volumes from 1973 to 1980, with a commentary by Heinrich Zoller and others. Recent exploration of Gesner's surviving manuscripts and the recog-

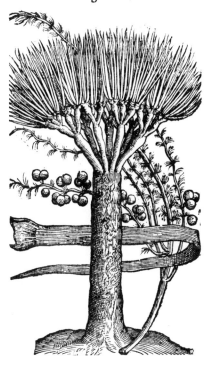

1 *Draco arbor*.
The Dragon tree.

Gerard *Herball*, ed. Johnson, Dragon tree (*Dracaena draco*), p. 1523.

1 Plantin's original blocks were used for the last time in the 1636 Gerard.

2 Also written Conrad Gessner.

Van der Borcht collection Dragon tree (*Dracaena draco*). See also Arber (1986), plate xxii.

Mattioli *De Plantis Epitome*
Cyclamen, p. 357.

D'Aléchamps *Historia Generalis*
Plantarum Cistus, vol. I, 232.

nition of other relevant material, like his 'letters to scholars all over Europe which may yet be discovered . . . might shed some new light on the history of science as well as on the life of a man who personified the Renaissance ideal of the humanist as a universal scholar'.[1]

Some of the best of the Gesner–Camerarius woodcuts, which are of interest to botanists in that they pay attention to 'vegetative and floral characters', are to be found in Camerarius's edition of Mattioli's *De Plantis Epitome* (Frankfurt, 1586) and Camararius's own *Hortus Medicus* (Frankfurt, 1588). The flower book recording in fine watercolours the contents of Camerarius's garden in the 1580s was sold at Christie's in May 1992 and is now at the University of Erlangen.

For this same reason, only minimal space can be spared for the works of a number of distinguished French, Swiss and Franco-Swiss botanists such as d'Aléchamps and the brothers Bauhin.

Jacques d'Aléchamps (1513–88), one of the most erudite French plantsmen of his day, was another of Rondelet's many pupils to achieve distinction, though more as a compiler than as an original researcher. His *Historia Generalis Plantarum* appeared anonymously in Lyons in two volumes in 1587 and 1586, 'Pars Altera' being the first to be published. Most of the figures were appropriated from the usual sources – Mattioli, Fuchs, and the Plantin pool; they were cut in Lyons, and in fact made their first appearance in a French translation of Mattioli. We reproduce one of them to show the curious *horror vacui* of the engraver, which impelled him to scatter falling petals and flying insects to fill the empty backgrounds.

The two Bauhins, Jean the Younger (1541–1613) and Gaspard (1560–1624), were sons of a French physician, Jean the Elder, who on becoming a Protestant fled his native Amiens to settle in Switzerland, where his children were born. Six successive generations of the family were doctors. Jean the Younger was befriended by Fuchs, botanized with Gesner, and at Montpellier helped d'Aléchamps with his *Historia* until, like his father, he was driven from France by religious persecution. His *magnum opus*, which was not published in its entirety until long after his death, was his *Historia Plantarum Universalis* (Yverdon, Switzerland, 3 volumes, 1650–51). It contained lucid descriptions of about five thousand species and owed much to the assistance of his son-in-law, Jean-Henri Cherler.

Gaspard Bauhin, a slow developer, lived to outstrip his much older and more precocious brother. After studying at various universities in Switzerland, Italy, Germany and France he produced several distinguished botanical works of which his *Prodromos* (Frankfurt, 1620) and *Pinax Theatri Botanici* (Basel, 1623) were the most influential. *Pinax* means 'register' or 'chart'. Many subsequent botanists – including Linnaeus, who, says Arber, received a copy of the second edition of the *Pinax* 'as payment for giving lessons in botany to a fellow medical student' – made considerable use of his writings, and in the opinion of Sachs it was with Gaspard Bauhin that the progress of botanical science at that time reached its zenith 'as regards both the naming and description of individual plants and their classification according to likeness of habit'.[2]

1 Wellisch (1975), p. 171.
2 Hunt *Catalogue*, vol I (1958), 343.

The Herbal in England

Where the printed herbal is concerned, England was sadly slow off the mark. Even the famous – one might almost say, notorious – Gerard was to add nothing to the development of botanical illustration; and, as we have already said, Banckes's *Herball* of 1525, the first book printed in England devoted solely to herbs, was unillustrated.

The Grete Herball of the following year was simply *Le Grant Herbier* or *Arbolayre*[1] 'translated out of ye Frensshe into Englysshe' and carrying the same little medieval figures, its only novelty being a brief appendix on wines. It deserves mention merely because of the impact it made in England. Its aim was purely practical, though in this respect its illustrations did little if anything to help. Some of the figures are made to serve for two different plants – for example, in the *Arbolayre* the same one was used for the cherry (*Prunus* sp.) and the deadly nightshade (*Atropa belladonna*); but fortunately it bore so little resemblance to either that it can have caused few if any deaths. In *The Grete Herball* it represents the cherry and the tormentil (*Potentilla tormentilla*).

bytternesse ben called damacenes/and the other agryotes. Cheryes ben good to cete

The Grete Herball 'Cherry, cap. cxxxix, and 'tormentil', cap. liii.

Arber deals at length with the book's delightfully quaint text, and points out that some of the recommended uses of the herbs – liquorice and horehound for coughs; laudanum, henbane, opium and lettuces as narcotics, for example – are still found acceptable. 'The compiler of *The Grete Herball* noted that the "iuce of the leves of wilows is good to delay the heate in fevers yf it be dronken"; if he could return now, and see the extent to which drugs based on salicylic acid are used for this purpose, he would feel that his statement had been confirmed to an extent of which he could scarcely have dreamed.'[2]

It is entertaining, if not very helpful, to learn that the compiler (quoting Galen) mistrusts the use of water for most purposes: 'Many folke that hath bathed them in colde water have dyed or they came home', and 'It is unpossyble for them that drynketh overmoche water in theyr youth to come to the aege that god ordeyned them.' It may or may not be that 'to make folke mery at ye table, take foure leves and foure rotes of vervayne in wyne, than spryncle the wyne all about ye hous where the eatynge is and they shall be all mery.' But such matters should not concern us here.

William Turner (1510/15–68), physician, divine and 'the father of British botany', was a cantankerous Protestant whose violently proclaimed views involved him in long exiles abroad. His major (and only illustrated) work was his *New Herball*, the first part of which was published in London in 1551, the second (together with the first) in Cologne in 1562, and the whole work in three parts in Cologne in 1568. Its figures were taken from Fuchs, and the botanical importance of this and Turner's other publications must be read elsewhere.

Lyte's translation of (Clusius's translation of) Dodoens, published in London in 1578 as *A Nievve Herball*, was mentioned in the previous chapter.[3] The book – illustrated, of course, from the familiar Plantin pool – is, however, of great interest to students of English literature in that it was almost certainly the source of botanical knowledge for Edmund Spenser and Shakespeare. Arber[4] makes out a most convincing case for its

1 See p.114.

2 Arber (1953), p. 318; and see also Arber (1986), pp.44–50.

3 See p.156.

4 (1986), pp.126, 127.

direct influence on the 'Aprill Eclogue' in Spenser's *Shepheardes Calender*, which appeared a year after the publication of Lyte's book. Spenser died in 1599; but after 1597 Shakespeare would also have had access to the first edition of Gerard.

What are we to say of the first edition (1597) of Gerard(e)'s *Herball* – the Bible of English herbalists?

To criticize it seems almost blasphemy. Yet criticism is in order, for the truth is that its text is largely unoriginal and often corrupt, and its woodcuts, with very few exceptions, appropriated from the usual Continental sources. As Anderson puts it, Gerard should 'in all honesty be recognised as Dodoens' *Herbal* with English dress, manners, and substance'. But Gerard's many faults may almost be forgiven, for he wrote with the golden pen of the Elizabethan age. Take, for example, a line or two from his dedication to Lord Burghley: 'What greater delight is there than to behold the earth apparelled with plants, as with a robe of imbroidered worke, set with oriental pearles, and garnished with great diversitie of rare and costly jewels.' One is reminded of Sa'di's introduction to his *Gulistan* ('Rose Garden'), written more than three centuries earlier; if only the Persian had found an Elizabethan translator!

John Gerard (1545–1612) was born at Nantwich, in Cheshire, and apprenticed at the age of seventeen to Alexander Mason, a warden of the Barber-Surgeons – a company of which, many years later, the youth was to become master. He travelled – how, when, and in what circumstances we do not know – up the Baltic to Russia, and even inland from Narva as far as Moscow, before settling in London about 1577; possibly he made the voyage as ship's surgeon. A house in fashionable Holborn suggests that he was comfortably off, and his appointment as superintendent of Lord Burghley's town and country gardens that he moved in the best society; he also had his own garden in Holborn, of whose contents he published a *Catalogus* in 1596.

John Norton – printer, bookseller and publisher – encouraged by the success of Lyte's *A Nievve Herball*, had engaged a certain Dr Priest to make, and presumably annotate, a translation of Dodoens's final work, his *Pemptades*; but Priest died leaving his task unfinished, and Gerard found himself invited to take over. The question that still puzzles us is whether or not Gerard made unacknowledged use of Priest's translation, which is believed to have been almost complete at the time of his death. Dr Stephen Bradwell, in a prefatory letter in the eventually published work, seems to imply that he did; and Thomas Johnson, who was to produce a revised and enlarged edition of Gerard in 1633, stated there that Priest's translation 'became the ground-worke whereupon Mr Gerard built up this worke; but that it might not appear a translation, he changes the generall method of Dodonæus into that of Lobel.' (In fact this was not his reason: Dodoens's classification was essentially pharmacological, whereas Gerard had a different and a wider audience in mind.)

Gerard, however, in his 'Address to the Reader', wrote: 'Doctor *Priest* ... hath (as I heard) translated the last edition of *Dodonaeus*, which meant to publish the same; but being prevented by death, his translation likewise perished.' Arber maintains that 'this can only have been a deliberate lie', and that it was through carelessness that Gerard allowed Bradwell's letter to stand. Blanche Henrey, on the other hand, springs to Gerard's defence with a carefully reasoned argument too detailed to give here.[1] In any case, while the main substance of the *Herball* is admittedly derived from Dodoens's *Pemptades* and the works of several other botanists, it also contains delightful embellishments, some provoked by Gerard's own botanical forays and his keen interest in the English flora.

Gerard soon realized that he had taken on a task beyond his powers. When Norton rented nearly eighteen hundred woodblocks from Tabernaemontanus's Frankfurt publisher to illustrate the *Herball*, the embarrassed author found himself unable to match many of them with the text. Further, his Latin was notoriously poor, and it was even alleged (by Johnson) that he believed Fuchsius, with such a name, to be 'one of the ancients'. Norton, warned of all this by a friend, called in l'Obel, who had already corrected more than a thousand errors before Gerard, further soured by an acute attack of ague, lost his temper and accused l'Obel of knowing no English. L'Obel responded by accusing Gerard of using material from his *Adversaria* without acknowledgement. Norton, sick of these endless delays, agreed with Gerard that the book should be printed immediately – faults and all.

Gerard readily admitted his share in the book's shortcomings, and Johnson was later to lose no opportunity to attribute most of them to him. 'Faults,' wrote Gerard, 'I confess have escaped, some by the printers oversight, some through defects in my self to performe so great a worke, and some by meanes of the greatnesse of the labour.' It was 'a worke, I confesse, for greater clerks to undertake, yet may my blunt attempt serve as a whetstone to set an edge upon some sharper wits, by whome I wish this my course discourse might be both fined and refined.' This is exactly what was to happen.

The Bodleian Library possesses a superb hand-coloured copy (pressmark L1.5.Med) of Gerard, presented to Sir Thomas Bodley by John Norton in 1601. From it we reproduce the title-page[2] and the portrait of the author at the age of fifty-three, both engraved on metal by William Rogers, and four other leaves with woodcut figures.

So far as the production of the book is concerned, a whole world separates its elegant humanistic type from the heavy 'black letter' of Lyte's *Nievve Herball* of less than twenty years earlier; yet this appearance of modernity is only skin-deep. Of more than two thousand illustrations only eighteen are original, among the most interesting of the latter being the first woodcut of the potato, a plant he had already listed in his unillustrated *Catalogus* of 1596. It was thanks to Gerard that for many years the true home of the potato was believed to be Virginia, not Chile. The portrait of Gerard at the end of the preliminaries, mysteriously dated 1598, shows the author holding a rose[3]; it was to be used again,[4] this time reversed, on the title-page of the 1633 Johnson edition.

The most notorious, though not original, woodcut in the *Herball* is that of 'the breede of Barnakles'. Gerard relates that barnacle trees, which occur in northern Scotland and the

1 Henrey (1975), vol. I, 35–54, gives by far the best brief account of Gerard's *Herball*. The discussion of the Priest affair begins on p.45.

Gerard *Herball* Potato (*Solanum tuberosum*), p. 781.

2 For a detailed description of this, see Margery Corbett (1977). See also colour plates pp. 150–51, 154–55, and the two illustrations in black and white on this and the following page.

3 This has usually been assumed to be a potato, but the Bodleian coloured copy makes it look more like a rose.
4 See p. 167.

Britannicæ Concha anatifera.
The breede of Barnakles.

Gerard *Herball* 'Barnacle tree', p. 1391.

1 See p.172.

'Orchades' (Orkneys), grow shells which on opening hatch out geese. He admits at first to hearsay only, but he forfeits our confidence in his veracity when he continues (the italics are ours):

But what our eies have seene, and hands have touched, we shall declare. There is a small Ilande in Lancashire called the Pile of Foulders, wherein are found the broken peeces of old and brused ships, some whereof have beene cast thither by shipwracke, and also the trunks or bodies with the branches of old and rotten trees, cast up there likewise; whereon is found a certaine spume or froth, that in time breedeth unto certaine shels, in shape like those of the muskle, but sharper pointed, and of a whitish colour; wherein is contained a thing in forme like a lace of silke finely woven, as it were togither, of a whitish colour; one ende whereof is fastned unto the inside of the shell, even as the fish of Oisters and Muskles are; the other ende is made fast unto the belly of the rude masse or lumpe, which in time commeth to the shape and forme of a Bird: when it is perfectly formed, the shel gapeth open, and the first thing that appeereth is the foresaid lace or string; next comes the legs of the Birde hanging out and as it groweth greater, it openeth the shell by degrees, till at length it is all come foorth, and hangeth onely by the bill; in short space after it commeth to full maturitie, and falleth into the sea, where it gathereth feathers, and groweth to a foule, bigger than a Mallard, and lesser than a Goose.

It is not so much Gerard's credulity that we deplore as his false claim of autopsy. The myth was still widespread, though Albertus Magnus had exploded it, by personal observation, more than three centuries earlier, and Fabio Colonna[1] had stoutly rejected it in his *Phytobasanos* of 1592. Arber makes the rather charming, but unacceptable, suggestion that 'it may be that a shadow of the myth still lingers in our speech when we call an unfounded rumour a *canard*.'

In 1629 John Parkinson produced his *Paradisus* (of which more presently), a florilegium equivalent in popularity to Gerard's *Herball*. In his introduction he mentioned that if this is 'well accepted' it will speed up a projected sequel, 'A Garden of Simples', intended no doubt to supersede Gerard's — a work by then more than thirty years old, whose imperfections were each year becoming more apparent.

John Norton had long been dead, and in 1632 his firm passed into the hands of Adam Islip, Joice Norton and Richard Whitaker(s), who decided to beat Parkinson to the post by swiftly producing an enlarged and emended edition of the original work which Thomas Johnson, a London apothecary, agreed to undertake. What is usually known as 'Johnson's Gerard' appeared in 1633 (reprinted in 1636), and in it Johnson complains bitterly that he 'was forced to perform this task within the compasse of a year.' Most authors, as they observe the vastness of the undertaking, will marvel at Johnson's almost superhuman industry and deplore the inhumanity of his publishers.

Gerard *Herball*, ed. Johnson, title-page.

Johnson's Gerard, which was published at 42*s*. 6*d*. unbound and 48*s*. bound, is half as long again as Gerard, contains 2765 woodcuts almost all taken from a different source (mostly the Plantin pool), and is in every respect immeasurably superior to its predecessor. This Johnson rather unpleasantly stresses in his address 'To the Reader' (which opens with a survey of botany from Solomon to Parkinson), and after listing many of Gerard's shortcomings smugly declares, 'Divers such things there are, which I had rather passe over in silence, than here set downe: neither should I willingly have touched hereon, but that I have met with some that have too much admired him, as the only learned and judicious writer. But let none blame him for these defects' – for, in short, he did his best: he simply was not properly qualified to do the job.

Gerard *Herball*, ed. Johnson,
Bananas (*Musa paradisiaca*), p. 1516.

A few of the figures were drawn by Johnson himself,
including, on page 1516 of the *Herball*, the famous bunch of
bananas, which is also shown in a vase in the bottom lefthand
corner of the frontispiece engraved by John Payne. Johnson
writes: 'Aprill 10. 1633. my much honoured friend Dr *Argent*
(now President of the Colledge of Physitions of London) gave me a
plant he received from the Bermuda's.' After describing the plant
in some detail – it was, in fact, merely a branch – he continues:

> The fruit which I received was not ripe, but greene, each of
> them was about the bignesse of a large Beane; the length of
> them some five inches, and the bredth some inch and halfe:
> they all hang their heads downewards, have rough or
> uneven ends, and are five cornered; and if you turne the
> upper side downeward, they somewhat resemble a boat, as
> you may see by one of them exprest by it selfe . . . The stalke
> with the fruit thereon I hanged up in my shop, where it
> became ripe about the beginning of May, and lasted until
> June: the pulp or meat was very soft and tender, and it did
> eate somewhat like a Muske-Melon. I have given you the
> figure of the whole branch, with the fruit thereon, which I
> drew as soone as I received it . . . I have been told (but how
> certainely it is I know not) that the floures which precede
> the fruit are bell-fashioned, and of a blew colour . . . Some (as
> our Author hath said) have judged it the forbidden fruit;
> othersome, the Grapes brought to *Moses* out of the Holy-
> land.

Gerard, who had described the banana in 1597 and illustrated it
with two different figures (also included by Johnson), calls it 'in
English, Adams Apple tree'.

Johnson fought bravely on the Royalist side in the Civil War
and died of a wound received during a skirmish while taking part
in the defence of Basing House in September 1644.[1] Anthony
Wood wrote of him that he was 'no lesse eminent in the Garrison
for his valour and conduct, as a Souldier, than famous throughout
the Kingdom for his excellency as an Herbarist, and Physician'.

1 According to R. G. C. Desmond,
*Dictionary of British and Irish
Botanists* (London, 1977), Johnson
was born *c.* 1597. The *D.N.B.* says
'probably early in the seventeenth
century'. Both Edmund Gosse and
the Hunt *Catalogue* give the
impossible date of 1561, which
would mean that Johnson was
mortally wounded in battle at the
age of eighty-three! Powell and Kew
(1932) settle for *c.* 1600.

Parkinson *Paradisus*, title-page.

The swift action on the part of Gerard's publishers in producing Johnson's revised edition of Gerard's *Herball* in record time delayed the appearance of Parkinson's herbal for seven years.

John Parkinson (1567–1650) was born in Nottinghamshire and trained as an apothecary, but no details of his life appear to be known until we find him established in London in 1616 with a garden of his own in Long Acre. He was appointed Apothecary to James I and subsequently 'Botanicus Regius Primarius' to Charles I. His two principal works were *Paradisi in Sole Paradisus Terrestris*, that is, 'Park-in-Sun's Park on Earth' (1629,[1] 1656 with minor emendations, and a facsimile of the first edition in 1904), and *Theatrum Botanicum: the Theater of Plantes, or An Universall and Complete Herball* (1640). The former he described as a 'Feminine [Worke] of Flowers' and he dedicated it to Queen Henrietta Maria; the latter, a 'Manlike Worke of Herbes and Plants', was dedicated to Charles I.

[1] John Tradescant the Younger's own annotated copy of the first edition of the *Paradisus* is in the Bodleian Library. It also has notes in the hand of Elias Ashmole.

We have been hard put to it to find a justification for the inclusion of the *Paradisus* in this book. It is true that some of the hundred and more full-page woodcuts, each showing seven or eight different plants, are indeed original; but many are not, and most are almost as crudely cut as those of the pre-Brunfels era. Further, the major part of the text is a florilegium, though this is followed by accounts of 'A Kitchen Garden, or Garden of Herbes' and an 'Orchard'. But the real reason for giving space to this enchanting work is the irresistible temptation to reproduce its engagingly naïve title-page.

Unlike those of the two Gerards and Parkinson's herbal, this is a woodcut, not a metal-engraving, and is the work of 'A. Switzer',[1] who was also responsible for the less successful figures in the text. It shows the Garden of Eden, with Adam, scarcely taller than a cyclamen, plucking an apple from the Tree of Knowledge (though surely it was Eve who did this?) and Eve gathering a flower which a botanist would have some difficulty in identifying. Among the remaining flora, most of it easily recognizable, may be mentioned the notorious 'vegetable lamb of Tartary' or 'borametz'. This 'plant-animal',[2] whose existence was reported by 'divers good authors', was said to grow 'about Samarcanda', and had been almost universally believed in for at least four centuries.

'From a Paradise of pleasant Flowers,' wrote Parkinson at the beginning of his *Herball*, 'I am fallen (*Adam* like) to a world of profitable Herbes and Plants . . . namely those plants that are frequently used to helpe the diseases of our bodies.'

Everything, he told the readers of his new book, had conspired to delay its publication, and he had even felt obliged to change its 'note' from 'A Physicall Garden of Simples' to 'A Theater of Plantes':

> The disastrous times, but much more wretched and perverse men have so farre prevailed against my intended purpose, and promise, in exhibiting this Worke to the publicke view of all; that their extreame covetousnesse had well nigh deprived my Country of the fruition; But having at last, though long and with much adoe, broken through all obstacles opposing *tandem prodiit in lucem.*[3]

It is not hard to guess that those 'perverse men' were Norton's successors. But Parkinson, unlike poor Johnson, did at least have a decade rather than a twelvemonth in which to do his work. *Theatrum Botanicum: the Theater of Plantes, or, An Universall and Complete Herball*, as it is described on its title-page, was printed and published in London in 1640 by Thomas Cotes. This charming page, the work of William Marshall, shows a half-length portrait of the author holding a flower – one of the Compositae, or daisy family, though which of its thirteen thousand species it would be hard to guess. On either side of the title stand, as in Johnson's Gerard, two figures – here not Theophrastus and Dioscorides but Adam (with spade) and Solomon (with sceptre) – while the four corners of the design represent the fauna and flora of the four continents (the Asian damsel nonchalantly riding a great one-horned Indian rhinoceros is particularly engaging).

1 For the problem of identification of this Switzer see Henrey (1975), vol. I, 161–63.

2 It was probably based on a misunderstanding of the Asiatic cotton-plant (see H. Lee, *The Vegetable Lamb of Tartary*, London, 1887).

3 '. . . it reached the light at last' (that is, the book had appeared).

170

The text describes more than three thousand plants – almost double the number in Gerard and even more than in Johnson's Gerard. It runs to 1755 folio-sized pages – truly, as he states, 'an herball of a large extent' – and is divided into seventeen 'classes or tribes': '1 Sweet Smelling Plants; 2 Purging Plants; 3 Venemous, Sleepy, and Hurtfull Plants, and their Counter-poysons; 4 Saxifrages, or Breakestone Plants', and so on. It concludes with '17 Strange and Outlandish Plants' – in which the vegetable lamb has fittingly found a place, though Gerard's goose-bearing barnacle tree was apparently considered *too* outlandish for inclusion.[1]

The woodcut illustrations – we cannot bring ourselves to count them – are for the most part freshly cut but inferior copies of those in Johnson's Gerard. This may in part account for the fact that although Parkinson's text is the more original, his herbal never attained the popularity of its predecessor; but it must also be remembered that some of those who already possessed Johnson's Gerard may well have felt that enough is enough. A striking figure in Parkinson's *Herball*, one not to be found in Johnson's Gerard, is that of the yucca (*Yucca gloriosa*); it first occurs in the *Paradisus*, but is so confused there with other plants that its merits are not immediately apparent.

Parkinson's *Herball* also provides us with the first record in Britain and accompanying figures of several interesting native plants, in particular the Welsh poppy, *Meconopsis cambrica* – 'in many places in *Wales*'; the now almost extinct lady's slipper orchid, *Cypripedium calceolus* – 'in a wood called *Helkes* in *Lancashire* neere the border of *Yorkeshire*', and the strawberry-tree, *Arbutus unedo* – '[that] hath beene of late dayes found in the west part of *Ireland*'.

Parkinson died in London in 1650 and was buried in the old church of St Martin-in-the-Fields in what is now Trafalgar Square – then still, appropriately, a relatively rural spot for the ashes of the great flower-lover. His legacy to the world was his still-popular *Paradisus* and his no less valuable though less remembered *Theater of Plantes* – the last great English herbal to be published with woodcut illustrations. Vast in bulk, wide in scope (as its title-page indicates) and almost impossible to lift, regrettably it was never issued – as were Fuchs, Bock and Mattioli – in portable form or, indeed, even reprinted in folio. Though herbals with metal-engraved figures continued to appear, as will be told in the final part of this book, Parkinson's *Theater of Plantes* marks the end of an epoch.

As a tailpiece to our account of the English woodcut herbals we will mention very briefly the *Botanologia: the English Herbal, or History of Plants*, a handsome folio published in 1710 and dedicated to Queen Anne, by that remarkable quack, William Salmon (1644–1712). Its metal-engraved title-page[2] is attractive but the botanical woodcuts, though apparently original, are of no great interest. Richard Pulteney, writing eighty years later, dismissed the text as 'beneath all criticism'. The story of the author's amazing rise from mountebank's assistant (by way of Salmon's pills – a panacea for every ailment at 3*s.* a box) to relative respectability is entertainingly told by Dr Norman Moore in the *Dictionary of National Biography*.

1 The unicorn's horn, though hardly a vegetable, has however also been reported upon since it served as a test for poisoned drinks, and Parkinson readily accepts that the animal may be found 'farre remote from these parts, and in huge vast Wildernesses among other most fierce and wilde beastes'.

Parkinson *Theatrum Botanicum* Yucca (*Yucca gloriosa*), p. 153.

2 By Michael van der Gucht after a drawing by Eloas Knight. It is reproduced on page 6 of Henrey (1975), vol. 2.

The Metal-Engraved Herbals

For over a hundred years woodcuts and metal-engravings were both being used to illustrate herbals, but gradually the work of the etchers and engravers spread from the title-pages to take over the illustrations in the rest of the books.

The distinction between woodcutting and wood-engraving finds an echo in the difference between etching and engraving on metal. In etching, the copper plate, which is the medium for both processes, is covered with a layer of varnish on which the design is scratched with a needle. The plates are then steeped in an acid solution which attacks any part of the surface from which the varnish has been removed, thus fixing the pattern into the metal. Engraving is a more laborious process, for a tool called the burin is used to cut the design into the plate. Both processes print from an intaglio surface, that is, ink is forced into the lines cut or etched into the metal before the rest of the plate is wiped clean and the design transferred to paper.

Woodcuts and wood-engravings are usually printed at the same time as the text they accompany, but metal-engravings need printing separately, on a press in which the plate and the paper are pushed together between rollers. The inked lines of the plate then leave an impression in relief on the paper. As compensation for the greater labour, and the consequent extra cost of the books employing it, there is the increase in precision and detail that engraving allows.

Among the earliest herbals with illustrations engraved on metal is one of the rarest, that of Pietro di Nobili, published in Rome about 1580. Di Nobili is known as an engraver of maps and a publisher in the second half of the sixteenth century. Only two copies of his herbal – both imperfect – are recorded, one at Kew, the other in the Hunt collection at Pittsburgh. It contains about thirty plates, each divided into quarters holding a drawing of a plant, its name, and a note of its medicinal use. The plate showing 'Xiphio' (a gladiolus) and 'Alisma' is reproduced here.

Fabio Colonna's *Phytobasanos* ('Plant Touchstone'), published in Naples in 1592, is another of the earliest herbals with illustrations printed from metal, although the thirty-seven etched plates appear within woodcut borders of the ornaments known as printers' flowers, which were printed with the text. Colonna (1567–1650), a lawyer by profession, began his botanical investigations of Dioscorides in an attempt to identify the herb recommended for the treatment of epilepsy, from which he suffered. His research led him to try valerian, with apparent success, and his descriptions of the plants of Dioscorides and other classical authors were collected in the *Phytobasanos* and a later book, *Ekphrasis* ('Description'), similarly illustrated and published in Rome in two parts in 1606 and 1616.

Some of Colonna's original drawings for these books are now in the Biblioteca Nazionale in Naples. The etchings made from them are botanically accurate as well as attractive, often including separate details of flowers and fruits, as well as the Greek and Latin names of the plants. Colonna is believed to have been his

Nobili *Herbal* Xiphio (*Gladiolus* sp.) and Alisma, plate 18.

Left
Reneaulme *Specimen Historiae Plantarum* Sunflower (*Helianthus annuus*), p.83.

Below
Colonna *Phytobasanos* Dogbane (*Apocynum venetum*), p. 111.

own artist and engraver, and his work earned the praise of Thomas Johnson, who described him as 'a man of an exquisit judgment' in the preface to the second edition of Gerard's *Herball*. A fine copy of the *Phytobasanos*, now in the Bodleian Library (pressmark 4° Z 35 Art.) was given by the author to Clusius, who noted this fact at the bottom of the title-page in his beautifully neat italic hand, adding the date of receipt, 1593.

Twenty-five etchings which, though not much larger than Colonna's, show a more sophisticated technique and much greater sensitivity, are found in the *Specimen Historiae Plantarum* of Paul Reneaulme (or Renealmus), published in Paris in 1611. Reneaulme (1560–1624), a physician (and therefore a botanist) who was a native of Blois, describes each plant in detail, with a care reflected in the loving observation shown in the illustrations. His sunflower shows the back of the shaggy blossom and its curling stalk at the bottom of the plate, as well as a full-face sun-shaped flower above, and the stem appears in two sections, to give an idea of its great height. With the exquisite representation of each part of the plant, the lack of colour seems irrelevant, and even the thin paper on which the book is printed, allowing the shadow of the type on the back of the page to show through, cannot spoil the beautiful clarity of the plates.

Each description starts with a discussion of the plant's name, including Greek and sometimes French, German, Italian, Spanish, and even Arabic equivalents. A detailed account of the appearance of the plant follows, with a note of its flowering season and country of origin if it is not a native. The sunflower, for example, 'blooms in August and has been brought from Peru to form a not unworthy addition to our gardens.' Notes on virtues and medicinal uses, if any, are added.

A supplement to Reneaulme's book contains five botanical poems by Jacques-Auguste de Thou (1553–1617), ranging in subject from lilies to cabbages.

During the seventeenth century botany began to emerge as an independent science, slowly outgrowing what Rousseau[1] later described as its first misfortune: 'Le premier malheur de la Botanique est d'avoir été regardée dès sa naissance comme une partie de la Médecine.' Marcello Malpighi in Italy and Nehemiah Grew in England were pioneer students of plant anatomy, while Magnol and Tournefort in France and John Ray and Robert Morison in England were exploring the relationships and classification of the plants they were describing. Botany, from being 'one of the handmaids of physick' (so described by William Coles in 1656), was finding an identity of its own.

The herbal tradition was not transformed into modern botany overnight, and books reflecting the pattern of earlier herbals continued to appear. A handful of the more important or interesting of these has been selected to illustrate the continuation of the theme to the end of the eighteenth century, a kind of dying fall as herbalism gave way before botany.

Tournefort's *Élémens de Botanique*, published in 1694 as a manual of the scheme of classification developed by its author, suffered a sea change in translation and emerged in English twenty-five years later as *The Compleat Herbal*, extended by 'large additions from Ray, Gerarde, Parkinson, and others, the most celebrated Moderns'. The additions included notes on the virtues and medicinal uses of the plants, but the translator was sensible enough to keep the original illustrations, the work of Claude Aubriet, and indeed to mention them on his title-page as 'about Five Hundred Copper Plates . . . all curiously Engraven'. The translation has been attributed to John Martyn, later professor of botany at Cambridge, who was certainly the translator of Tournefort's book on the flora of the region round Paris, but Blanche Henrey has recently pointed out the lack of evidence to confirm this attribution. *The Compleat Herbal* is usually found in two volumes dated 1719 and 1730, although it was issued in parts, one of the earliest botanical books to appear in such a form. The first part was published in April 1716, when Martyn was only sixteen years old.

Joseph Pitton de Tournefort (1656–1708) became professor of

1 Rousseau's introduction to his *Fragmens pour un Dictionnaire des Termes d'Usage en Botanique* was published in volume IV of his *Mélanges* in 1782, and included in Thomas Martyn's 1785 translation of his *Lettres Élémentaires sur la Botanique*, written in the years 1771 to 1773 and published in the same volume of the *Mélanges*.

botany at the Jardin Royal in Paris in 1683, and his pupils there included Sir Hans Sloane, whose collections were later the nucleus of the British Museum, and William Sherard, who re-established the Botany School at Oxford. The system of classification described by Tournefort in his *Élémens* and in its later, enlarged, Latin version, *Institutiones Rei Herbariae* (1700), depended on the structure of the flower. In spite of its condemnation by Ray and other botanists, the scheme was widely accepted until Linnaeus's work on classification in the eighteenth century rearranged the systematics of the world's fauna and flora.

His illustrator, Claude Aubriet (1665–1742), was already employed as an assistant to Jean Joubert, the artist engaged in adding to the royal series of plant portraits, when Tournefort commissioned the illustrations for his *Élémens*. The engravings are remarkable for their accuracy, including minutely detailed dissections, probably reflecting the botanist's close supervision of his artist's work. The original drawings and proof copies of the plates are now in the Muséum National d'Histoire Naturelle in Paris. One of the title-pages to each volume of the *Élémens* is a view of the Jardin Royal, engraved by Vermeulen, showing the plan of the garden, with a mount in one corner, and a glimpse of the botany school, where Tournefort taught. Aubriet himself is probably best remembered today by the familiarity of aubrieta, the favourite garden plant named after him and so often and so variously mis-spelled.

Among William Sherard's books in the Botany School at Oxford there is an unusual large-paper copy of Aubriet's illustrations to the *Élémens* (pressmark Sherard 673), as well as a complete set of the ordinary version of the book. The engraved title-page is there, but without a volume number, and the impressions of the plates are particularly fresh and clear. The crown imperial (*Fritillaria imperialis*) shown is reproduced from this copy. William Sherard (1659–1728) was a botanist who followed his Oxford education with travels in Europe. He studied under Tournefort in the late 1680s, and later corresponded with him. He also spent several years as consul at Smyrna before returning to England, where his collections of plants and books enriched the Oxford Botany School, and his bequest later provided a salary for the professor.

Tournefort *Élémens de Botanique*
Crown imperial, plate 197.

Elizabeth Blackwell's *Curious Herbal*, published in weekly parts and collected in two large volumes in 1737 and 1739, is the odd result of the lady's attempt to free her husband from financial embarrassment. The rescue seems to have succeeded, only to be overtaken by a worse difficulty, for after some years Alexander Blackwell moved to Sweden, where he became involved in a plot to alter the succession to the throne. He was charged with high treason and executed in 1747. His wife, who had not gone to Sweden with him, died in 1758, and was buried in the Chelsea churchyard.

The *Curious Herbal* is closely associated with the garden of the Society of Apothecaries at Chelsea, as the industrious artist – she drew, engraved, and coloured all five hundred plates herself – took a house nearby in Swan Walk in order to collect fresh plants as she needed them. The Chelsea Physic Garden, which is still there although no longer possessing a river frontage to allow access by barge, was founded in 1673. John Evelyn, visiting it in August 1685, was able to admire 'a collection of innumerable rarities ... Particularly, besides many rare annuals the Tree bearing the Jesuits bark [the source of quinine], which had don such wonders in quartans'. As a practical gardener he was also interested in the heating of the conservatory: 'What was very ingenious [was] the subterranean heate, conveyed by a stove under the Conservatory, which was all Vaulted with brick.' Sir Hans Sloane, having studied there himself in his student days, acquired the freehold in 1712 and ten years later granted a lease in perpetuity to the Society of Apothecaries. A statue of this benefactor by Rysbrack now presides over the walled garden, which is still a centre for botanical teaching, in association with various colleges of the University of London.

A preliminary announcement, signed by several eminent physicians and apothecaries, presumably helped to collect subscribers to the serial parts of the *Curious Herbal*, and Mrs Blackwell's illustrious patrons, including Sir Hans and many leading members of the Royal College of Physicians, can have done nothing to hinder the sale of her book. The various issues of it, and there are pirated as well as genuine ones, are copiously supplied with appropriately grateful dedications. In Elizabeth Blackwell's own words:

> This work has met with a more favourable reception from the publick, both at home and abroad, than I could have expected, knowing my own insufficiency for the undertaking; this success must be ascrib'd in great measure to the prevailing influence of those worthy gentlemen, who kindly honoured it by their recommendation.

Blackwell *Curious Herbal* Fig (*Ficus carica*), vol. I, 125.

The book's reputation remained high to the end of the century, in countries abroad as well as on its own ground. An enlarged version with a Latin text added to the English one, *Herbarium Blackwellianum*, was published in Nuremberg in five volumes from 1750 to 1760, edited by Christoph Jacob Trew, with the plates redrawn and engraved by N. F. Eisenberger. A supplementary volume to this edition, adding over a hundred extra plates, followed in 1773.

Blackwell's original drawings are in the Oak Spring Garden Library in Virginia, but the prints, coloured or uncoloured, in the book are rather stiff. Each plate has a polyglot list of common names, the contribution of Alexander Blackwell, and the engraved text includes brief descriptions of the plants and their uses, heavily indebted, as the introduction makes plain, to Joseph Miller's *Botanicum Officinale*, 'an account of all such plants as are now used in the practice of physick', published in 1722. Occasional butterflies or other insects crawl among the plants.

An Italian herbal of about the same date as Elizabeth Blackwell's is Giambattista Morandi's *Historia Botanica Practica*, published in Milan in 1744, with a second edition in 1761. Little seems to be known of this author, but there is a large collection of his drawings in the Turin botanic garden, and a volume of botanical manuscripts and pen-and-ink studies, some of them the originals of the printed ones, in the botany library of the British Museum

Morandi *Historia Botanica Practica*
Thyme, hyssop and other plants,
plate XXVIII.

(Natural History). The Society of Herbalists (London) once owned
another volume of drawings, until it was sold by auction at
Sotheby's in July 1958.

The printed book is found in both coloured and uncoloured
states. It contains nearly seventy large plates packed with plants,
sometimes as many as ten to a page, apparently drawn from living
specimens. There are some details of flowers and fruits, although
these are not always easy to see in the dense undergrowth. A
relatively uncrowded page, showing some sense of design, is
illustrated. Morandi was his own engraver, and his text includes
descriptions of the plants and notes on their virtues and
medicinal uses.

The books of Sir John Hill (1716?–75) include several that give
advice on medicinal plants, although they form only a tiny part of
his vast literary output, ranging from plays, translations, and
miscellaneous journalism to the twenty-six folio volumes of his
Vegetable System, which earned him the Swedish Order of Vasa,

and a treatise on the virtues of honey. So various were the subjects of his writings that, according to the *Dictionary of National Biography*, even Hannah Glasse's *Art of Cookery* (1747) was once wrongly attributed to him. His other professional activities included medicine – he was trained as an apothecary – acting and horticulture.

Hill's quarrelsome character and his battles with, among others, the Royal Society, Henry Fielding and David Garrick, seem to have cast a long shadow, for until the recent work of Blanche Henrey brought all the evidence together, his courtesy title was often printed in inverted commas to cast doubt on its authenticity. It now appears that his title, like that of the far more respectable Sir William Chambers, was granted by George III in recognition of the Swedish honour. Hill was also in charge of the royal gardens at Kensington Palace, and was later associated with the establishment of one of the gardens at Kew that now form part of the Royal Botanic Gardens there.

Hill's *Useful Family Herbal* was first published anonymously in 1754, but the author acknowledged his work the following year, in the second edition. It was intended 'to inform those who live in the country, and are desirous of being useful to their families and friends . . . of the virtues of those plants, which grow wild about them', so that the plants could be used to relieve illness. The book, an octavo, has eight plates with six small drawings on each, in alphabetical order of their English names, to match the text. The herbal, which also contains advice on the collection and preparation of herbs, was popular and useful enough to run into several more editions over the next half-century.

In 1756 Hill's *British Herbal*, a much more imposing book, began to be issued in weekly parts. The series was completed early the following year, when a version with coloured illustrations was also offered, as a whole book or, once again, in weekly instalments. There are seventy-five plates in the book, each one crowded with plants. The illustration used here shows mallows and other herbs. The plates are allegedly engraved 'after originals done from nature by the author', but occasional ones indicate that the engraver also drew the original. Many engravers were involved, including Hill himself. Henry Roberts was responsible for the plate shown, and also for the allegorical frontispiece, drawn by Samuel Wale and showing the Genius of Health receiving the tributes of the four continents – two white, one black, one coffee-coloured – and delivering them to a clamouring crowd of British Readers. The herbal includes plants 'cultivated for use, or raised for beauty', exotic as well as native. To the descriptions and virtues of them are added occasional notes that go beyond the purely medicinal: 'Liquorice is a celebrated medicine . . . A kind of beer may be brewed with liquorice in the place of malt, and it will have a considerable strength and an agreeable flavour.' Perhaps it might also have a colour to rival that of Guinness.

The *British Herbal* began to appear only three years after the publication of Linnaeus's *Species Plantarum*, and, although Hill frequently criticizes Linnaeus's botanical innovations, he also makes occasional use of binomial names, that is, names composed of two Latin words, for the plants he is describing. Linnaeus's book, published in 1753, became the starting-point of modern

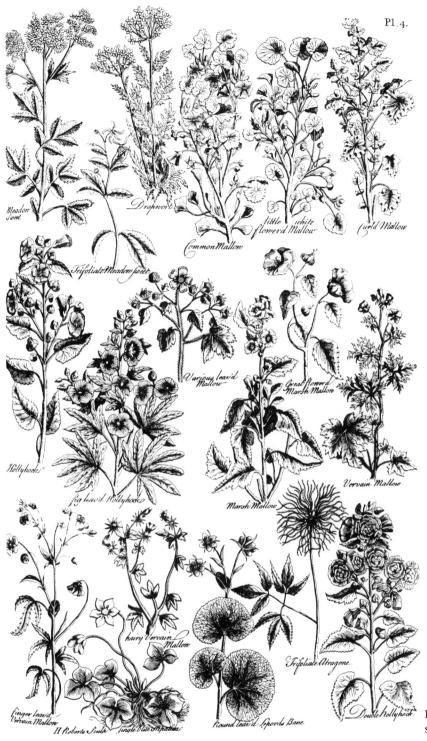

Pl. 4.

Meadow Sweet

Dropwort

Common Mallow

little white flower'd Mallow

Curl'd Mallow

Trifoliate Meadow sweet

Various leav'd Mallow

Great flower'd Marsh Mallow

Hollyhock

fig leav'd Hollyhock

Marsh Mallow

Vervain Mallow

finger leav'd Vervain Mallow

hairy Vervain Mallow

Round leav'd Leports Bane

Trifoliate Atragone

H Roberts South

Single Blue Hepatica

Double Hollyhock

Hill *British Herbal* Mallows (*Malva* sp.) and other plants, plate 4.

botanical nomenclature on this pattern, and William Stearn has made it plain that Hill's book contains the earliest valid descriptions of a few plants, the hart's-tongue fern, *Phyllitis vulgaris*, among them.

Hill's herbal career continued with the Latin *Herbarium Britannicum*, two small volumes published in 1769 and 1770, before he returned to English in the *Virtues of British Herbs*, which appeared in 1770 with illustrations based on those of the *Herbarium*. The Latin book was aimed at the physicians, the English 'fitted for general service, and in our own tongue'.

Perhaps the neatest epitaph on Sir John Hill is Dr Johnson's: he was 'an ingenious man, but had no veracity'.

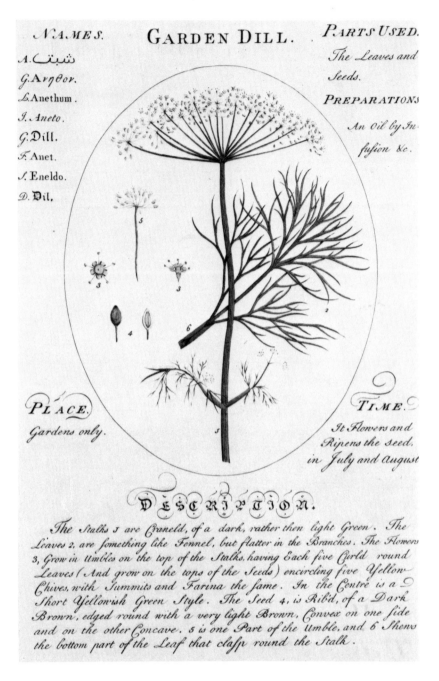

The illustration within the oval frame is labelled:

NAMES.

GARDEN DILL.

PARTS USED.

A. شبت

G. Aνηθον.

L. Anethum.

I. Aneto.

G. Dill.

F. Anet.

S. Eneldo.

D. Dil.

The Leaves and Seeds.

PREPARATIONS

An Oil by Infusion &c.

PLACE.

Gardens only.

TIME.

It Flowers and Ripens the seed, in July and August

DESCRIPTION.

The Stalks 5 are Craneld, of a dark, rather then light Green. The Leaves 2, are something like Fennel, but flatter in the Branches. The Flowers 3, Grow in Umbles on the top of the Stalks having Each five Curld round Leaves (And grow on the tops of the Seeds) encircling five Yellow Chives, with Summits and Farina the same. In the Centre is a Short Yellowish Green Style. The Seed 4, is Rib'd, of a Dark Brown, edged round with a very light Brown, Convex on one side and on the other Concave. 5 is one Part of the Umble, and 6 Shews the bottom part of the Leaf that clasp round the Stalk.

Sheldrake *Botanicum Medicinale* Dill (*Anethum graveolens*), p. 33.

A herbal apparently less popular than Elizabeth Blackwell's or John Hill's was Timothy Sheldrake's *Botanicum Medicinale* or 'an herbal of medicinal plants in the College of physicians list', published in parts about 1759, with a second issue a decade later. The complete book contains about 120 engravings, for the most part made by C. H. Hemmerich from Sheldrake's drawings. The text is also engraved on each plate – names in various languages, description, and virtues in neat copperplate writing, arranged around and beneath an oval frame containing the illustration of the plant, with details of the flowers and other parts. The pictures are charming and sufficiently lifelike to help fulfil Sheldrake's purpose, which he described as 'to . . . prevent Mistakes in the use of Simples . . . to illustrate, and render such Herbals as want the just Representations in their proper Figures and Colours more useful'.

Sheldrake (fl.1736–56), having failed as a saddler in Norwich, became a distiller and followed his earlier interest in natural

180

history with the study of appropriate books on botany and drugs. He later moved from Norwich to London, perhaps on the advice of Sir Hans Sloane, whose help he sought. On the title-page of *Botanicum Medicinale* he is referred to as 'the late ingenious T. Sheldrake'; he probably died in the late 1750s.

The French botanist Pierre Bulliard (1742–93) began to publish his *Herbier de la France* in Paris in 1780, and the enormous series of coloured plates[1] – about six hundred of them – continued to appear in thirteen annual parts until the artist's death. Bulliard was his own engraver, and the illustrations were printed in colour, instead of the colour being added by hand to the engraved outline. One plate was made for each colour and the series printed in perfect register to produce the final soft, delicate colouring. The process used was aquatint, engraving on a plate given a grain by powdered resin.

1 See colour plates pp.158–59.

Parts of the *Herbier* were issued separately, about eighty plates as an *Histoire des Plantes Vénéneuses et Suspectes* in 1794 and again in 1798, and, from poisonous plants turning to more useful ones, an *Histoire des Plantes Médicinales*, containing 125 illustrations, in 1809. Another large group of illustrations formed an exhaustive catalogue of fungi.

A book that claimed to be an account of Chinese medicinal plants was published in Paris in 1781 by Pierre Joseph Buc'hoz (1731–1807), who has been described as the French equivalent of Sir John Hill. This large folio is called *Herbier, ou Collection des Plantes Médicinales de la Chine*, and is allegedly copied from a manuscript in the library of the Emperor of China. No text or description gives advice on the use of the plants, although the Chinese names are listed. This book and others among the avalanche of them produced by Buc'hoz used drawings by native Chinese artists at a time when interest in the Orient was becoming extremely fashionable. The series of *Mémoires sur les Chinois*, compiled by the French Jesuits living there, appeared during the last quarter of the eighteenth century, and Britain sent an embassy to the Emperor in 1792 and another in 1816. The drawings used by Buc'hoz, though decorative, have little botanical value, and look as though they would be more at home on a fabric design.

Buc'hoz himself was a lawyer before taking up medicine and spending some time as physician to Stanislaus, King of Poland. He soon gave up this office to become what might be called a literary hack, producing book after book on botany, medicine, mineralogy, agriculture, ornithology, and etymology, as well as many smaller tracts and brochures. This flood of print contained little or no original material, and nothing to bring the author the recognition of contemporary naturalists. He was accused of compiling his own books from those of others, and he certainly practised economy in the use of illustrations, the same plates appearing in more than one of his botanical works. As sales decreased, Buc'hoz tried anonymous publication, with no better fortune. The outbreak of the Revolution completed his ruin, from which he was rescued by a friend of his late wife's, who married him. A final echo of Hill is provided by the angry writings of his later years, attacking the world that refused to recognize his versatile genius.

Turkey Rhubarb

Culpeper's English Physician, ed. Sibly, Turkey rhubarb (*Rheum palmatum*), Plate 8.

It seems amazing that the innumerable editions of Culpeper's herbal, first published under its original title of *The English Physitian* in 1652, should have had to wait until late in the eighteenth century for illustrations other than the author's portrait. The first to add engravings of plants was Dr Ebenezer Sibly (1751–*c.* 1800), whose 1789 enlarged, quarto edition was also the first to call the book a 'complete herbal' in its subtitle. This edition, in a multitude of variant forms, was reprinted many times. Sibly was an astrologer, reflecting Culpeper's bias, but the aim described in his preface seems sensible enough: 'It requires that the practice of physic, instead of being clothed in a mystic garb, should be put upon a level with the plainest understanding, and the choice and quality of our medicines be rendered as obvious and familiar as our food.' Culpeper's text forms the first part of the book, followed by nearly thirty plates with a dozen or two plants illustrated on each one. Then comes an appendix by Sibly, adding descriptions and illustrations of foreign plants, including 'Turkey rhubarb' (*Rheum palmatum*). The growth of medicinal rhubarb in Britain was promoted by the Society for the Encouragement of Arts, Manufactures, and Commerce, now the Royal Society of Arts, and in 1770, once seed of the 'true rhubarb' was available, the Society offered a gold medal to the person raising the greatest number of these valuable plants.

Another enlarged edition of Culpeper's herbal, 'with several hundred additional plants, principally from Sir John Hill', and about two hundred unsigned plates, was produced in two volumes in 1792 by Joshua Hamilton. The plates to be coloured were printed on thicker paper, but copies often contain a mixture of black-and-white and coloured illustrations. This version seems to have been less popular than Sibly's, to judge by its lack of reprints.

William Curtis (1746–99) is probably best known for his huge and beautiful *Flora Londinensis* and for the *Botanical Magazine*, founded by him in 1787 and still surviving. In 1786 he began to publish *Assistant Plates to the Materia Medica, or Figures of Such Plants and Animals as are used in Medicine*. This small book, or rather the two sections of it that were issued, was aimed at medical students – 'We wish these plates to fall into the hands of every student who reads the Dispensatories' – for Curtis had noticed 'medical gentlemen most intimately conversant with the effects of herbs, with whose exterior form they are totally unacquainted'. Curtis was also a nurseryman and a former apothecary and 'Demonstrator of Plants' at the Chelsea Physic Garden, but his attempt to improve the student doctors' botanical knowledge seems to have been a failure. Publication ceased after only twenty illustrations, grouped in two decades, had appeared. Each tiny, accurate engraving faces a list of references to the appropriate standard books of the day, and those wishing to consult 'more splendid works' were referred to the herbals of Elizabeth Blackwell and Timothy Sheldrake.

Curtis *Assistant Plates* Foxglove (*Digitalis purpurea*), p. 3.

Neither artist nor engraver signed Curtis's *Assistant Plates*, but both the original drawings and the engraving may have been the work of James Sowerby (1757–1822), the first of the dynasty of botanical and conchological artists of that name, who was working for Curtis at the time. Sowerby was definitely responsible for both stages of the excellent illustrations to Dr William Woodville's *Medical Botany*, which was issued in parts, collected into three volumes and a supplement, from 1790 to 1795. James Sowerby, after studying at the Royal Academy Schools, was apprenticed to the marine painter Richard Wright, but later he deserted the sea to concentrate on flower painting. As well as working for Curtis as both artist and engraver, he contributed illustrations to many other important books of the period, including *English Botany* (with text by James Edward Smith, the founder of the Linnean Society of London), published from 1790 to 1814.

William Woodville (1752–1805), a Quaker physician from Cumberland, attempted to describe all the plants included in 'the catalogues of the materia medica, as published by the Royal colleges of physicians of London and Edinburgh', where he was trained. No one since Blackwell and Sheldrake had tried to produce an illustrated account on such a scale: the three volumes and the supplement contain nearly three hundred plates, coloured or uncoloured. Each of the three volumes bears an appropriate dedication, the first to the Royal College of Physicians of London, the second to James Edward Smith, President of the Linnean Society, and the third to the Royal College of Physicians of Edinburgh. A second edition of the book appeared in 1810, and a third, revised and enlarged by W. J. Hooker and G. Spratt, in 1832. It remained the standard

Helleborus niger.

Published by Dᵣ Woodville April 1. 1790.

Woodville *Medical Botany* Hellebore
(*Helleborus niger*), vol. I, Plate 18.

illustrated book on the plants of the British pharmacopoeia until the late 1870s, when *Medicinal Plants*, by Robert Bentley and Henry Trimen, appeared.

The last book to be described appeared a little after our limit of 1800, but its charm is perhaps enough to break the barrier. Joseph Roques (1772–1850), a doctor in Paris, published his *Plantes Usuelles* there in 1807 and 1808, the two volumes including about 130 plates. An enlarged second edition appeared thirty years later, declaring its aim of being a tool for domestic medicine. The small quarto described the distinctive characters and medicinal properties of both native and exotic plants, and the

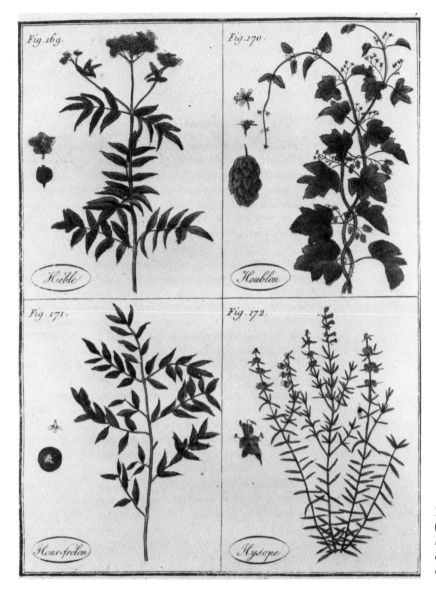

Roques *Plantes Usuelles* Elder (*Sambucus ebulus*), hop (*Humulus lupulus*), butcher's broom (*Ruscus aculeatus*), hyssop (*Hyssopus officinalis*), Plate 54.

illustrations, arranged four to a plate, are engravings 'coloured with the greatest care, produced by Grasset de Saint-Sauveur.

Roques' larger *Phytographie médicale* followed in 1821, just after the completion of François Chaumeton's *Flore médicale* (1814–20) in seven volumes with over 400 plates, most of them by P. J. F. Turpin (1775–1840), a fine, self-taught botanical artist who has always been a little overshadowed by Redouté. In an essay at the end of the book Turpin said that the brush was almost more use to the botanist than the pen, as drawings may tell more than words.

By 1800 botany's independent existence was well established, helped by the spread of Linnaeus's classification and nomenclature, but the link between botany and medicine, at every level from pure science to herbal folklore, is by no means broken. The search for new medicinal plants or new remedies from more familiar ones goes on, just as descriptions of the plants and their effects continue to be written. Within the last few years several more books on medical botany or healing drugs from plants have been published, but it seems safe to say that none of them can compete in either size or beauty with the greatest of their manuscript or printed predecessors.

Bibliography

ANDERSON, F. J.	*An Illustrated History of the Herbals.* New York, 1977
ARBER, Agnes	The colouring of sixteenth-century herbals. *Nature,* **145**:803–4, 25 May 1940. (Reprinted as a supplement to *Herbals,* 3rd edn, pp.315–18.)
	From medieval herbalism to the birth of modern botany. *Science, Medicine and History: Essays Written in Honour of Charles Singer,* edited by E. Ashworth Underwood, volume 1, pp.317–36. London, 1953. (Reprinted as a supplement to *Herbals,* 3rd edn, pp.319–38.)
	Herbals: Their Origin and Evolution. 3rd edn, with an introduction and annotations by William T. Stearn. Cambridge, 1986.
BARKER, Nicolas	*Two East Anglian Picture Books.* London, 1988.
BARLOW, H. M.	Old English herbals, 1525–1640. *Proceedings of the Royal Society of Medicine, Section of the History of Medicine,* **6**:108–49, 1913.
BAUMANN, F. A.	*Das Erbario Carrarese.* Bern, 1974.
BECKER, G. and others	*Tournefort.* Paris, 1957.
BEHLING, Lottlise	*Die Pflanze in der mittelalterlichen Tafelmalerei.* Weimar, 1957.
BLUNT, Wilfrid	*The Art of Botanical Illustration.* London, 1950. (Revised edition edited by W. T. Stearn, 1994.)
BRITTEN, James	Morandi's *Historia Botanica Practica. Journal of Botany* (London) **56**:212–17, 1918.
BRUMBAUGH, Robert S. and others	*The Most Mysterious Manuscript: The Voynich 'Roger Bacon' Cipher Manuscript.* Carbondale, Illinois and London, 1978.
CALLERY, B. G.	Ancients, moderns and reliable friends: stated sources of some English herbals. *Journal of the Society for the Bibliography of Natural History,* **8**:435–44, 1978.
COCKAYNE, Oswald	*Leechdoms, Wortcunning, and Starcraft of Early England,* vol. 1. London, 1864.
COGLIATI ARANO, Luisa	*The Medieval Health Handbook: Tacuinum Sanitatis,* translated and adapted by Oscar Ratti and Adele Westbrook. London and New York, 1976.
CORBETT, Margery	The engraved title-page to John Gerarde's *Herball or Generall Historie of Plantes,* 1597. *Journal of the Society for the Bibliography of Natural History,* **8**:223–30, 1977.
EMMART, E. W.	*The Badianus Manuscript.* Baltimore, 1940.
FINAN, J. J.	Maize in the great herbals. *Annals of the Missouri Botanic Garden,* **35**:149–91, 1938.
FISCHER, Hermann	*Mittelalterliche Pflanzenkunde.* Munich, 1929.
GANZINGER, Kurt	Ein Kräuterbuchmanuskript des Leonhart Fuchs in der Wiener Nationalbibliothek. *Südhoffs Archiv für Geschichte der Medizin,* **43**:213–24, 1959.
GESSNER, Conrad	*Historia Plantarum facsimileausgabe Aquarelle aus dem botanischen Nachlass von Conrad Gessner (1516–1565),* edited by H. Zoller, M. Steinmann, and K. Schmidt. Zurich, 1973–80.
GOFF, F. R.	Johann Petri of Passau and his *Herbarius Latinus. Festschrift für Claus Nissen zum Siebzigsten Geburtstag 2 September 1971,* edited by E. Geck and G. Pressler, pp.302–10. Wiesbaden, 1973.
GREENE, E. L.	*Landmarks of Botanical History,* edited by Frank N. Egerton. Stanford, 1983. (Volume I first published in 1909.)
GUNTHER, R. W. T.	*The Greek Herbal of Dioscorides.* Oxford, 1934.
	The Herbal of Apuleius Barbarus (MS Bodley 130). Oxford, 1925.
HENREY, Blanche	*British Botanical and Horticultural Literature before 1800.* London, 1975.
HUNGER, F. W. T.	*The Herbal of Pseudo-Apuleius.* Leiden, 1935.
HUNT, R. M. M.	*Catalogue of Botanical Books in the Collection of Rachel McMasters Miller Hunt,* compiled by Jane Quinby and Allen Stevenson. Pittsburgh, 1958–61.
JACKSON, B. D.	[Engraved copies of illustrations from the *Codex Vindobenensis* and the *Codex Neopolitanus.*] *Proceedings of the Linnean Society of London,* **129**:2–3, 1916–17.
JEFFERS, R. H.	*The Friends of John Gerard.* Falls Village, Connecticut, 1967–69.
JESSEN, C. F. W.	*Botanik der Gegenwart und Vorzeit.* Leipzig, 1864. (Reprint, Waltham, Massachusetts, 1948.)
JOHNSON, J. de M.	A botanical papyrus with illustrations. *Archiv für Geschichte der Naturwissenschaften,* **4**:403–8, 1912.
JOHNSTON-SAINT, P.	Deux herbiers manuscrits du XVe siècle au Musée Wellcome de Londres. *Aesculape,* ns **28**:244–50, 1938.
KEIL, Gundolf	Hortus Sanitatis, *Gart der Gesundheit, Gaerde der Sunthede,* in *Medieval Gardens,* edited by Elisabeth B. MacDougall (Dumharton Oaks Colloquium on the History of Landscape Architecture IX), pp.55–68. Washington, 1986.
KLEBS, A. C.	Incunabula lists. I. Herbals. *Papers of the Bibliographical Society of America,* **11**:75–92, 1917 and **12**:41–57, 1918.
MARCUS, M. F.	The herbal as art. *Bulletin of the Medical Libraries Association,* **32**:376–84, 1944.
NISSEN, Claus	*Die botanische Buchillustration.* 2nd edn. Stuttgart, 1966.
	Herbals of Five Centuries. Zurich, 1958.
OPSOMER, Carmélia and STEARN, W. T.	*Livre des Simples médicines: Codex Bruxellensis IV.1024, a Fifteenth-Century French Herbal.* Antwerp, 1981–2.

PÄCHT, Otto	Early Italian nature studies and the early calendar landscape. *Journal of the Warburg and Courtauld Institutes,* **13**:13–47, 1950.
	Die früheste abendländische Kopie des Illustrationen des Wiener Dioskurides. *Zeitschrift für Kunstgeschichte,* **35**:201–14, 1975.
PAYNE, J. F.	On the *Herbarius* and *Hortus Sanitatis. Transactions of the Bibliographical Society,* **6**:63–126, 1901.
PLANTIN-MORETUS MUSEUM	*Botany in the Low Countries (end of the 15th century – ca. 1650).* Antwerp, 1993.
PUTNAM, Clare	*Flowers and Trees of Tudor England,* London, 1972.
RAPHAEL, Sandra, and others	*The Mattioli Woodblocks.* London, 1989.
ROHDE, E. S.	*The Old English Herbals.* London, 1922. (Reprint, London, 1974.)
RYTZ, Walther	Das Herbarium Felix Platters. *Verhandlungen der Naturforschenden Gesellschaft in Basel,* **44**:1–222, 1933.
	Pflanzenaquarelle des Hans Weiditz. Bern, 1936.
SCHMID, Alfred	*Ueber alte Kräuterbücher.* Bern, 1939.
SCHREIBER, W. L.	*Die Kräuterbücher des XV und XVI Jahrhunderts.* Munich, 1924. (Supplement to a facsimile of Peter Schöffer's *Hortus Sanitatis (Gart der Gesundheit).)*
SERRA, L.	*L'Arte nel Theatrum Sanitatis.* Rome, 1940.
SINGER, Charles	*From Magic to Medicine,* London, 1928.
	The herbal in antiquity and its transmission to later ages. *Journal of Hellenic Studies,* **47**:1–52, 1927.
	Herbals, *Edinburgh Review,* **237**:95–112, 1923.
SOLINAS, Francesco	L'erbario miniato e altri foglie di iconografia botanica appartenuti a Cassiano dal Pozzo, in *Il Museo Cartaceo di Cassiano dal Pozzo* (Quaderni Puteani I), pp.52–76. Milan, 1989.
	l primo erbario azteco e la copia romana de Cassiano dal Pozzo, in *Il Museo Cartaceo di Cassiano dal Pozzo* (Quaderni Puteani I), pp.77–83. Milan, 1989.
SPRAGUE, T. A.	The evolution of the herbal. *South-Eastern Naturalist,* **43**:33–39, 1938.
	The herbal of Otto Brunfels. *Journal of the Linnean Society, Botany,* **48**:79–124, 1928.
and NELMES, E.	The herbal of Leonhart Fuchs. *Journal of the Linnean Society, Botany,* **48**:545–642, 1931.
STANNARD, Jerry	Alimentary and medicinal uses of plants, in *Medieval Gardens,* edited by Elisabeth B. MacDougall (Dumbarton Oaks Colloquium on the History of Landscape Architecture IX), pp.69–91. Washington, 1986.
	P. A. Mattioli: sixteenth-century commentator on Dioscorides. *Bibliographical Contributions, University of Kansas Libraries,* **1**:59–81, 1989.
STEARN, W. T.	From Theophrastus and Dioscorides to Sibthorp and Smith: the background and origin of the *Flora Graeca. Biological Journal of the Linnean Society,* **8**:285–98, 1976.
	Hill's *The British Herbal* (1756–7). *Taxon,* **16**:494–98, 1967.
	The historical background to the illustrations of the *Herbarium Apulei* and *Herbolario volgare,* in a facsimile edition of the *Herbarium Apulei,* pp.xliii–lxxi. Milan, 1979.
THOMPSON, C. J. S.	*The Mystic Mandrake.* London, 1934.
WELLISCH, Hans	Conrad Gessner: a bio-bibliography. *Journal of the Society for the Bibliography of Natural History,* **7**:151–247, 1975.
	Early multilingual and multiscript indexes in Herbals. *Indexer,* **11**:81–102, 1978.

Index

The index includes names of people and plants and titles of books and manuscripts. English plant names are used, with occasional Latin ones when there is no English equivalent. Page numbers in italics refer to illustrations or their captions. A small n after a page number refers to a footnote.

Acknowledgments

The authors would like to thank the staffs of the libraries that own the books and manuscripts described, especially Gavin Bridson of the Linnean Society, E. J. Freeman of the Wellcome Institute for the History of Medicine, Sandra Ward of the Royal Botanic Gardens, Kew, and John Brindle of the Hunt Institute for Botanical Documentation.

They are also grateful to Dr David Mabberley for help with the identification of some of the plants pictured, Dr David Howlett and Dr Robert Allen for advice on texts and translations, and Dr Marcus Graham for the naming of a moth included in one of the illustrations. Mrs May Macdougall's notes on the Pierpont Morgan Dioscorides manuscript were also most valuable.

Permission to quote from the 1938 edition of Agnes Arber's *Herbals*, which is still one of the most important books on the subject, has been given by its publishers, Cambridge University Press. The authors are also grateful to Messrs Collins for use of material from the 1950 edition of Wilfrid Blunt's *The Art of Botanical Illustration*.

Picture acknowledgments